ENGLISH
DAY
BY
DAY

ENGLISH
DAY
BY
DAY

MICHAEL RODDY

Academic Therapy Publications
Novato, California

Betty Lou Kratoville, Editor

ISBN: 0-87879-668-1

8 7 6 5 4 3 2 1 0 9
5 4 3 2 1 0 9 8 7 6

Library of Congress Cataloging-in-Publication Data

Roddy, Michael, 1945-
    English Day by Day / Michael Roddy.
        p. cm.
    ISBN 0-87879-668-1 (soft)
    1. English language–Textbooks for foreign speakers. I. Title.
PE1128.R634 1989
428.2´4–dc19   88-27428
                                                                                CIP

Contents

For My Family

Note: If students in your class find the exercises in this intermediate-level workbook too challenging, you will want to use the entry-level workbook, *BEGINNING ENGLISH DAY BY DAY*. Order #907-9 available from Academic Therapy Publications.

To the Teacher

Many dedicated people stand ready to serve the needs of adult students who are resolved to master English as their second language. It's a demanding teaching assignment that requires commitment, caring, and creativity. And since the field is comparatively new, certainly in terms of numbers (waiting lists for ESL adult programs continue to grow throughout the country), ESL teachers are constantly searching for meaningful materials and frequently decide to create their own to augment those already in the marketplace. Such a teacher is Michael Roddy of the San Mateo High School District Adult School, who saw a need and rose to fill it with the material in this book.

English Day by Day aims to meet the needs of students who want to learn English for any number of significant reasons: to further their vocational education, to get a better job, to enroll in higher education, or simply to meet the demands of everyday situations that regularly occur in shopping, banking, housing, health care, et cetera.

The book stresses the basic language skills of grammar, reading, writing, and pronunciation in the context of real life situations where competency in written and conversational skills and in problem-solving techniques can be critical. The format is sequential and uncomplicated. There are 13 units with 9 sections in each unit as follows:

I. Vocabulary

In order to prepare the student for more effective participation in the activities of the unit, lists of key words are introduced, separated into applicable subject areas, and occasionally reinforced with relevant illustrations. Students may be encouraged to look up the words in their own language dictionaries when necessary. The teacher should pronounce and explain each word. This helps to establish just how much the students already know and where their experience from their own countries lies in this subject area. For example, in a unit on banking, an "expert," such as a former bank teller, can enrich the classroom experience by adding insight and relevance to the meaning of the vocabulary words. Brainstorming is often helpful and reinforcing. The illustrations are "think pieces" that have been included to provide additional room for discussion. The main idea in this section of the unit is to establish the theme and to set the tone for what is to follow in the unit.

II. Getting Started

This section is designed to provide an informal bridge between the preceding vocabulary section and the more structured exercises that follow. Two photographs are presented that depict a partial aspect of the unit's theme. Students should be encouraged to talk about each photograph, what may be taking place in it, how this relates to their own experiences in the United States and in their native countries, and the differences between the two photographs. A hypothetical situation is presented at the end of this section to promote judgment and continued critical thinking.

III. Conversations

Three conversations, using the unit theme and related vocabulary and introducing some popular conversational idioms, are presented. This structured exercise gives students the opportunity to practice in pairs. A less structured "Dialogue Puzzle" follows in which pairs of students can work together to construct their own dialogue, using appropriate statements to the responses that have been provided and vice versa. The last part, "Discussion," gives students an opportunity to respond personally and somewhat informally to some of the points discussed earlier in this section.

IV. Reading

Before the beginning of the reading section, another vocabulary list is introduced that includes some of the original unit words from Section I plus new words.

The reading selections deal with adult characters from other countries who are studying English in the United States. They are: Michiko—Japan; Maria—Colombia; Chris—Taiwan; Giovanni—Italy; Juan—El Salvador; Mohammed—Afghanistan; and Sabine—Switzerland. These characters are presented in situations that are sometimes humorous, sometimes serious. Sometimes they are alone, sometimes interacting with others—but always the selections clearly relate to the theme of the particular unit. Exercises follow each reading selection: comprehension or sequence selections, true or false summary statements, and an opportunity to use the vocabulary words in other contexts.

V. Structure

This section introduces basic grammar. The material is presented sequentially, and all of the examples and practice exercises clearly pertain to each unit's individual theme. Some of the grammar presented is fairly sophisticated. If the instructor feels that it is unnecessary for the student to master grammar at this level, he/she should feel free to move ahead to the next section. The yardstick should clearly be—Is mastery of this information critical to the student's oral and written language needs?

VI. Composition

The compositions are controlled exercises in which students need only fill in blanks with words whose form is hinted at. After filling in the answers, the students read the composition aloud. Section VI exercises throughout the book get progressively less controlled so that the student is given the opportunity to write more independently as he progresses.

VII. Pronunciation

The pronunciation section consists of practice drills of vowels and consonants, along with their contrasts with other vowels and consonants. Students can repeat the words after the teacher and then say them aloud on their own.

VIII. Life Skills

This section now presents practical examples of the life skills that have been mentioned throughout the unit. When necessary, a new, highly specialized vocabulary is introduced just prior to carefully related exercises. Students are asked to read and answer questions.

IX. Problem Solving

This concluding section allows the student to combine all of his language skills with vocabulary and other information learned throughout the unit and to apply these to a situation that requires critical thinking. In small groups he has the opportunity to put together his conversational, problem-solving, and cooperative learning skills.

It should be noted that this is not a workbook to be handed to a student for solitary contemplation and completion. To the contrary, it requires ongoing instruction—and it requires interaction—between the teacher and the student, and among class members. This is an active, involved instructional approach—not a passive one.

There is a deliberate attempt to integrate all aspects of language into a useful tool for everyday living in an English-speaking culture. It is the author's intention that the student will not only learn from and enjoy this book but also will feel challenged, in a very active sense, to apply all of the methods, exercises, and vocabulary presented to his own life.

UNIT 1

SHOPPING

When we buy something it's important to be aware of everything about that product: what it costs, what it's made of, and how safe it is. A careful consumer is a person who not only is helping himself but also helping make the world a better, safer place to live in. This unit will prepare us for communicating effectively in the most common buying situations.

Objectives

Competencies:
Clothing Labels
Department Store Directory
Comparison Shopping
Warranties

Structure
Nouns
Possessives and Suffixes
Present and Present Continuous Verbs

Pronunciation:
long e (ē)
long e (ē) / short i (ĭ)
TH

I. Vocabulary

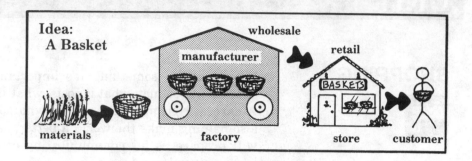

Idea: A Basket

materials — factory — wholesale — retail — store — customer

manufacturer

BASKETS

A. Buying

1. cash
2. charge
3. charge account
4. check
5. credit

6. debt
7. credit card
8. finance charge
9. minimum payment
10. layaway plan

B. Consumer Information

1. consumer
2. manufacturer
3. retail
4. wholesale
5. sale/discount/clearance
6. bargain/deal
7. inexpensive/cheap/reasonable
8. expensive
9. unit price
10. product/merchandise

11. catalog
12. sample/floor sample
13. brand name/generic
14. price tag/list price
15. mark down
16. warranty/guarantee
17. label/warning
18. defect
19. model number/serial number
20. Better Business Bureau

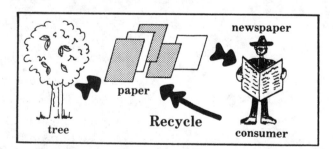

tree — paper — newspaper — consumer

Recycle

C. Ecology

1. recycle
2. pollution
3. energy-saving
4. non-allergenic

5. biodegradable
6. quality
7. no return/returnable
8. economy

II. Getting Started

Look at both pictures at the left and follow the directions below.

A.

B.

Picture A
1. Describe what's in the picture.
2. Name some good and bad things about shopping malls.
3. How does this picture compare with a shopping scene in your native country?

Picture B
1. Describe what's in the picture.
2. Why do people have garage sales?
3. Name some good and bad things about garage sales.
4. Do you have garage sales or something similar in your native country?

Pictures A and B
1. Describe those things that are the same in both pictures and those things that are different.
2. Roberto just got a job and is on a tight budget. He can pay the rent for his nice apartment plus all of the household expenses, but he really needs a lamp. Should he buy a new one at the mall or look for a used one in a garage sale?

III. Conversation

A.

1. Hi, Pat, this is Terry. How are you doing? I'm calling from the mall.
2. Hi, Terry, why are you shopping when you're in debt?

1. They're having a great factory clearance at the department store.
2. Are there any good bargains?

1. Plenty. Everything's reasonable.
2. I bet there are a lot of people there.

1. Yes, it's really crowded but worth it. I'm buying a refrigerator that's marked down a hundred bucks.
2. Sounds good. Do you have a charge account there?

1. Yes, I figure that I can afford the minimum payments every month.
2. I always pay with cash. I don't believe in plastic money or spending what you don't have.

B.

1. What are you doing here?
2. I'm returning this new jacket that has a hole in it.

1. That's terrible. Where are you taking it?
2. To the men's clothing department upstairs. It's a famous name brand, too.

1. Well, you can't trust everything nowadays. But you have your rights as a consumer.
2. Yes, there are guarantees against defects.

1. All in all, it's a hassle.
2. You can say that again.

C.

1. There's a no return on this bottle. I guess that means I can't take it back to the store.
2. You can take it to the recycling center, along with other glass items, or aluminum or paper. It saves our precious natural resources when we reuse things.

1. To be a good consumer you have to make sure that a product has quality.
2. And that it doesn't cause a lot of pollution to manufacture it.

1. Yes, the world's a small place and we have to take care of it. Use energy-saving appliances.
2. Good idea. I also use biodegradable soaps and other things that aren't allergenic—they're better for our health.

Dialogue Puzzle: With a partner fill in appropriate responses or questions in the spaces of the dialogue below, then practice and read to the rest of the class.

1. What are you thinking of buying?
2. _____

1. _____
2. No, I don't really need it.

1. _____
2. In _____ department store in the _____ shopping mall.

1. How do you get there?
2. _____

1. When does the sale end?
2. _____

Discussion: Answer the following questions about things talked about in the previous conversations.

- A. Do you have a credit card? What's good about it and what's bad about it?
- B. Did you ever buy anything that was defective?
- C. Did you ever recycle any products? Why or why not?

IV. Reading

A. Vocabulary

executive	sip	variety	consumer
branch	stare	items	aware
impressions	stationery	behaves	similar
experiences	correspondence	bargain	timid
a little while	mannequins	reasonable	jokes

B. Reading

Mrs. Michiko Tono writes a letter to her mother in Japan every Tuesday afternoon. Her letters contain her experiences and impressions of living in the United States. She also explains what her husband, a business executive of the branch of an import-export company, and their three-year-old boy, Seiji, are doing.

Right now Michiko is sitting at her desk, sipping a cup of tea, holding a pen, and staring at a blank piece of special stationery. She knows that before she starts, it always takes a little while to think of what to write.

About halfway through the letter, she writes:

> I like to shop for food at the American grocery stores twice a week and at the Japanese store on Saturday mornings. The Japanese store doesn't have enough products from our country, and nothing is really as fresh as we like it. I go shopping for clothes and household items at a nearby shopping mall that has two large department stores, a variety of fast-food restaurants, a jewelry store, a bakery, a record shop, and several other interesting stores. Seiji enjoys going there because he likes the mannequins, which he thinks are real, and the escalators. Usually he behaves rather well, but sometimes when he is too curious, he gets in trouble.
>
> I'm usually an aware consumer. I read the newspaper ads to find out when there are sales or just to compare prices of similar items in different stores. When the weather is nice, some Americans in this community like to have garage sales where they sell used things at reasonable prices. I'm still too timid with my English to shop at these places where you can sometimes bargain for an even lower price.

17

Americans like to use credit cards when they shop. The salespersons always say, "Cash or charge?" If you say that you want to pay in cash, they often ask if you want to apply for a credit card. My teacher at the adult school jokes about this when he says that buying on credit is a "national sport." We have a credit card but I prefer to pay with cash.

Well, I hope you're feeling well. Take care until our next correspondence. I miss you very much.

Your daughter,

Michiko

C. Exercises

1. Answer these questions.

a. When does Michiko write to her mother?

_____

b. What is on Michiko's desk?

_____

c. Why is Michiko staring at the blank paper?

_____

d. Is she satisfied shopping at the Japanese store? Explain.

_____

e. What fascinates Seiji at the mall?

_____

f. What happens at garage sales?

_____

g. Are credit cards popular in the United States?

_____

2. Write *true* or *false*.

_____ a. Michiko writes to her mother regularly.

_____ b. Seiji is an only child.

_____ c. The shopping mall has three department stores.

_____ d. Michiko finds out about sales by reading the newspaper.

_____ e. Michiko prefers to pay with cash.

_____ f. Michiko feels confident in her English.

_____ g. Michiko attends adult school.

3. Vocabulary: Put the vocabulary words from Section A (page 17) in the blank spaces.

    a. A good _____ must be _____ of any defects in a product before buying it.

    b. The _____ she writes on is _____ to yours. They both are light blue and have a picture of a bird on them.

    c. The woman business _____ likes to _____ her tea while reading the paper.

    d. The _____ little boy _____ well.

    e. The tourists are having a _____ of _____ on this trip. They are writing down their _____ of the country.

    f. The _____ in the store window always _____ out.

    g. My uncle usually _____ for _____ when he first meets you.

    h. Is she reading her _____ now?

    i. Be _____ . Use your head and _____ for a better price.

    j. The _____ of the tree is broken.

    k. There are many _____ on his shopping list.

V. Structure

Nouns

A noun is the name of a person, place or thing.

    Person: Kim, friend, customer, sister, manufacturer, Ms. Grady.

    Place: city, nation, Paris, store, China, lake, garden, mall, Better Business Bureau.

    Thing: account, catalog, pencil, sample, information, peace, truck, April, Ford, pollution.

Nouns are usually the subject or object of a sentence. In the sentence below, <u>salesperson</u> is a noun and the subject while <u>customer</u> is a noun and object.

    Sentence—Subject + Verb + Object

    The salesperson helps the customer.

Exercise S-1: Underline the nouns and indicate if they are the subject or object of the sentence.

    Example: The <u>woman</u> bought a second-hand <u>refrigerator</u>.
                S   *O*

    1. The consumer always recycles his aluminum cans.

    2. The mysterious credit card is creating too much confusion.

    3. Henry is buying a new refrigerator now.

    4. Advertising sometimes deceives consumers.

Plurals of Nouns

A. Most nouns add <u>s</u> to form the plural.

    counter-counters   label-labels

B. Add <u>es</u> to nouns that end in <u>s, sh, ch, x, z</u>.

    pass-passes   dish-dishes   watch-watches
    tax-taxes   buzz-buzzes

C. Change <u>y</u> to <u>i</u> and add <u>es</u> to nouns ending in a consonant plus <u>y</u>.

    sky-skies   baby-babies

Nouns that end with a vowel plus <u>y</u> only add <u>s</u> to form the plural.

    toy-toys   key-keys

D. Change <u>f</u> to <u>v</u> and add <u>es</u> to nouns ending in <u>f</u>.

    shelf-shelves

Change <u>fe</u> to <u>ve</u> and add <u>s</u> to nouns ending in <u>fe</u>.

    knife-knives

(There are some exceptions to this rule:

    belief-beliefs   safe-safes

Check an English dictionary to be sure.)

E. Add <u>s</u> to nouns ending in <u>o</u>.

    piano-pianos

Some nouns, however, add <u>es</u> to form the plural:

    hero-heroes   tomato-tomatoes

F. Some nouns have irregular plurals.

    child-children   tooth-teeth   foot-feet   ox-oxen
    mouse-mice   man-men   woman-women

G. Some nouns from other languages have irregular plurals.

    crisis-crises   phenomenon-phenomena

H. Some nouns are the same in both singular and plural.

    fish-fish   deer-deer

Exercise S-2: Write the plural for these nouns.

1. dress _____
2. shelf _____
3. bay _____
4. mouse _____
5. account _____
6. piano _____
7. salesman _____
8. crisis _____
9. warranty _____
10. hero _____
11. ox _____
12. sister-in-law _____
13. one box—five _____
14. a peach—some _____
15. his tooth—their _____
16. this potato—those _____
17. one life—many _____
18. a fish—some _____

20

Collective Nouns

Collective nouns are singular in form but plural in meaning.

family   team   group   flock   jury   class

Collective nouns have a singular verb if the idea of the noun is one.

The class is in the room.

A flock of birds usually flies by at noon.

Collective nouns are plural if the idea of the noun is many.

The class are discussing the lesson among themselves.

A flock of birds are eating different things on the beach.

Exercise S-3: Write the plural or singular verb for each sentence.

1. The team _____ well. (play, plays)

2. The jury members _____ arguing among themselves about different aspects of the trial. (is, are)

3. Her family _____ in Los Angeles now. (is, are)

Count and Noncount Nouns

Count nouns are nouns that you can count, such as dollars, suitcases, and glasses, while noncount or mass nouns are nouns you cannot count, such as money, luggage, and milk. A count noun may have a, an or one before it in the singular, and many or few before it in the plural; it may also end in s or es.

a floor sample   one payment   many checks

very few products

Noncount nouns are frequently names of substances or materials (bread, copper, cotton) liquids or gases (coffee, air) and abstract things (peace, beauty, happiness). They sometimes have much or little in front of them.

much money   little rice

You can put a lot of in front of both count or noncount nouns.

He likes a lot of furniture.   He likes a lot of chairs.

Here is a list of common noncount nouns:

advice	cash	information
news	housework	tennis
equipment	furniture	jewelry
luggage	machinery	money
water	rain	snow
wind	air	clothing
music	postage	damage
courage	education	traffic

21

fruit	food	butter
cheese	meat	milk
pepper	rice	salt
sugar	tea	transportation
intelligence	fun	happiness
luck	peace	violence
progress	safety	photography
pollution	vocabulary	poverty

Exercise S-4: Choose the correct word before the count or noncount nouns.

1. (much/many) He can't find _____ information in that book.

2. (little/few) She has very _____ friends.

3. (some/a) I'm cooking _____ meat.

4. (much/many) They are making _____ monthly payments.

5. (little/few) My cousin needs a _____ advice.

6. (some/a) Bob always adds _____ salt to his food.

7. (much/many) How _____ debts does he have?

8. (little/few) Mary drinks very _____ tea.

9. (Much/Many) _____ people like the new program.

10. (some/an) The company is buying _____ equipment for the office.

11. (is/are   much/many) There _____ too _____ poverty in that country.

12. (is/are   little/few) There _____ too _____ answers to the many problems.

Possessive Nouns

Possessive nouns indicate that an object belongs to someone or something.

A. All singular nouns: add 's.

    Jim's debts   the store's policy

        our friend's boutique   Mary's brother's credit card

B. Plural nouns that don't end in s: add 's.

    the children's furniture   the people's rights

C. Plural nouns that end in s: add '.

    The consumers' choice   the manufacturers' decision

Exercise S-5: Write the possessive noun.

1. the owner of the store _____

2. the decision of the women _____

3. the parking lot of those stores _____

4. the sale of the store of your cousin _____

Suffixes: Noun Endings

A suffix is the end part of the word that sometimes changes the word's function.

    She is inform<u>ing</u> the company. (Suffix—verb)

    She has all the informat<u>ion</u>. (Suffix—noun)

Exercise S-6: Add the correct suffix to form a word.

1. -NESS: kindness, business, happiness

   (sad) He can't forget his _____ .

2. -ION: location, information, protection

   (reflect) She is staring at her _____ in the mirror.

3. -MENT: appointment, statement, government

   (excite) There is a lot of _____ at the game.

4. -ANCE: performance, resistance, attendance

   (clear) There is a seven-foot _____ in that garage.

5. -ENCE: difference, existence, dependence

   (confer) They're having their national _____ in Los Angeles.

6. -URE: signature, expenditure, culture

   (press) The manager has to work under lots of _____ .

7. -ISM: consumerism, realism, alcoholism

   (hero) The newspaper is writing about the _____ of the woman who saved the child from drowning.

8. -ITY: necessity, capacity, eternity

   (able) The student has the _____ to do very well in college.

9. -ARY, -ERY, -ORY: burglary, bravery, factory

   (mission) He is a _____ from that church.

   (bake) The _____ opens early.

   (invent) They have a large _____ at that store.

10. -TUDE: attitude, solitude, longitude

   (fortify) He has a lot of _____ .

Exercise S-7: Add these suffixes to the main part of the words to form nouns; then put the completed words in the correct sentence.

-TUDE   -NESS   -ITY   -ISM   -ORY   -URE

nervous + _____ = _____

tour + _____ = _____

depart + _____ = _____

author + _____ = _____

soli + _____ = _____

deposit + _____ = _____

1. The plane's _____ is at 1 P.M.

2. _____ on that tropical island is a very big business.

3. Her _____ always bothers me.

4. They put all their valuables in the _____ .

5. That person who is alone seems to enjoy his _____ .

6. The manager has the _____ to OK that check.

Exercise S-8: Use the endings -MENT, -ENCE, -ANCE, -ION to change the underlined words into nouns. If necessary, consult your dictionary to find the correct root word.

1. Many students <u>attend</u> that class. There is always a large _____ .

2. The shoppers are <u>excited</u> about the big sale. There is a lot of _____ in the air.

3. The government is <u>investigating</u> the pollution problem. After the _____ they have to report it to the public.

4. He <u>depends</u> on his boss quite a bit. His wife doesn't like that kind of _____ .

5. His English <u>improves</u> all the time. The _____ pleases all of us.

6. She <u>intends</u> to return the defective merchandise but I'm not sure if that is her real _____ .

7. Those two products are <u>different</u> sizes. Can you notice the _____ ?

8. The youngsters always <u>enter</u> through the back door but the owner is telling them to use the front _____ next time.

Present and Present Continuous Verbs

A. Present

I work	I don't work	Do I work?
You work	You don't work	Do you work?
We work	We don't work	Do we work?
They work	They don't work	Do they work?
He works	He doesn't work	Does he work?
She works	She doesn't work	Does she work?
It works	It doesn't work	Does it work?

Present verbs describe a general or repeated (habitual) activity.

He works for Northern Airlines. (General activity)

She drives to work every day. (Repeated or habitual activity)

The short form of the present is as follows:

Do you like this? Yes, I do.

Does she pay her bills? Yes, she does.

Do they study there? No, they don't.

Does he have a credit card? No, he doesn't.

The following words of time are often used with the present:

always   often   sometimes   seldom   never
frequently   occasionally   rarely

Exercise S-9: Make a present sentence with each word of time above.

Example: They always go to the shopping mall.

_____

_____

_____

_____

_____

_____

_____

Exercise S-10: Write the correct present forms of the verbs in parentheses.

Example: (shop) Do you shop for groceries often?

1. (receive) _____ you _____ a lot of bills? Yes, I often _____ many.

2. (read) _____ she _____ ads for sales? No she _____ usually _____ any kinds of ads.

25

3. (check) _____ they ever _____ the labels before they wash the clothes? Yes, they _____ . (Short answer)

4. (pay) How _____ your cousin _____ for things? She frequently _____ with cash.

5. (buy) Where _____ you normally _____ your clothes? I _____ them at a place where there's quality and good prices.

6. (understand) _____ Harold _____ unit prices? No, he _____ . (Short answer)

7. (tax) _____ the government _____ the people? Yes, it _____ them.

B. Present Continuous

I am working	I'm not working	Am I working?
You are working	You aren't working	Are you working?
We are working	We aren't working	Are we working?
They are working	They aren't working	Are they working?
He is working	He isn't working	Is he working?
She is working	She isn't working	Is she working?
It is working	It isn't working	Is it working?

Present continuous verbs describe an activity in progress at the moment of speaking or an activity in progress over a period of time regarded as the present.

They <u>are</u> <u>speaking</u> Arabic with their mother <u>now</u>.

<u>I'm</u> <u>charging</u> my purchases <u>right</u> <u>now</u>.

<u>I'm</u> <u>studying</u> business administration in college <u>this</u> <u>year.</u>

<u>He's</u> <u>talking</u> with a client <u>at</u> <u>the</u> <u>present</u> <u>moment</u>.

The short form for the present continuous is as follows:

Are you reading that warranty now? Yes, I am.

Is he examining the sample? No, he isn't.

The verb work and live express the same meaning in both the present and present continuous.

Nancy lives with her sister now.

Nancy's living with her sister now.

Sam works at the shoe store.

Sam is working at the store now.

The verbs <u>know, believe, understand, like, want</u> and <u>prefer</u> don't usually use the present continuous.

Exercise S-11: Write the correct present continuous forms of the verbs in parentheses.

Example: (make) <u>Is</u> she <u>making</u> a list before shopping?

1. (plan) _____ he _____ to buy anything? No, he _____ to buy anything right now.

2. (think) _____ you _____ about opening an account here? Yes, _____ (Short answer.)

3. (take) _____ your friends _____ a bus downtown? Yes, they _____ one just about now.

4. (hand) _____ they _____ out free balloons at that new store? No, _____ . (Short answer.)

5. (go/check) _____ you and Miriam _____ over your budget for the month? Yes, we _____ all our expenses.

6. (try) _____ Erica _____ to find out which store has lower prices? No, she _____ to find out anything.

7. (show) _____ Mrs. Garcia _____ the salesperson her receipt? Yes, she _____ it to her now.

VI. Composition

Write words of your choice according to the description below each space. After you finish, let your teacher correct and then read aloud to the class.

_____ usually accompanies me when I go shopping
(person)

at _____ . The items that I seem to buy the most are
(place)

_____ . The prices of _____ and _____
(things)   (things)   (things)

are high while _____ and _____ are
(things)   (things)

generally low. I usually pay with _____ . If there is a
(type of payment)

big holiday sale, I _____ . The best kind of
(explain what you do)

merchandise to buy in the United States is _____ .
(thing)

The best things to buy in my native country are _____ .
(things)

Something that is difficult to find there to buy is _____ .
(thing)

The most popular department store there is _____ in
(place)

the city of _____ . Stores advertise by _____ .
(name of city)   (ways to advertise)

The most expensive thing to buy there is _____ while
(thing)

_____ is very reasonable. If a tourist goes there, I
(thing)

recommend that he buy _____ .
(thing)

27

VII. Pronunciation

A. Vowel:

long e ($\bar{e}$)

1. deal	2. recycle	3. retail
receipt	sleeve	warranty
eager	cheat	belief

4. These leaders believe in quality.
5. The saleslady treated them equally.

Contrasts:

long e ($\bar{e}$) / short i ($\breve{i}$)

6. eat/it	7. sleep/slip	8. steal/still
leave/live	cheap/chip	feet/fit
seat/sit	heal/hill	each/itch

B. Consonant:

TH (Voiced)

1. this	2. bother
theirs	weather
than	smooth

3. Are those going there another day?

TH (Unvoiced)

4. thing	5. healthy
thumb	anything
thief	strength

6. Beth is thinking of a new theme.

Contrasts:

7. bath/bathe
   breath/breathe
   ether/either

VIII. Life Skills

A. Clothing Labels

Vocabulary

Permanent Press—It needs little or no ironing. If you let out the hem, the crease stays.

Drip Dry—It dries quickly when hanging wet. It also needs little or no ironing.

Colorfast—It keeps original color with no fading or running.
Sanforized—Cotton cloth that is treated so it shrinks very little.
Preshrunk—Cotton cloth that will shrink a little more than Sanforized, but not very much.
Machine-washable—You can wash in a washing machine.
Hand Dry Only—Dry by hanging, not in a drying machine.
Dry Clean Only—A dry cleaners must clean it.
Waterproof—Water will not enter. Air won't either, so sometimes it's hot and sticky when wearing.
Water-repellent—Most water will stay off.
Flame Resistant—It will not burn.

Label Information:

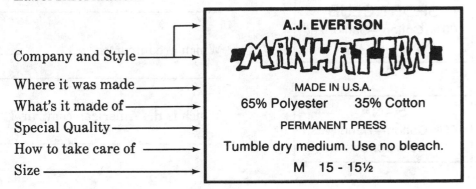

Company and Style	A.J. EVERTSON **MANHATTAN**
Where it was made	MADE IN U.S.A.
What's it made of	65% Polyester 35% Cotton
Special Quality	PERMANENT PRESS
How to take care of	Tumble dry medium. Use no bleach.
Size	M 15 - 15½

Kinds of Fabrics:

Natural

Cotton—Durable. Sometimes it shrinks.
Silk—Very elegant. You must handle with care.
Wool—Warm and durable. Be careful when cleaning.

Man-Made

Nylon—Strong and lightweight. It washes and dries easily.
Acrylic—Soft, warm and lightweight. Check label for cleaning.
Polyester—Resistant to wrinkling. It doesn't shrink.

Exercise L-1:

1. Lucia has a new dress with this label inside. When it's time to clean, what does she do?_____

_____

2. How does Kayoko clean her daughter's raincoat? _____

_____

HAND WASH DRIP DRY
1.

WIPE CLEAN WITH DAMP CLOTH 100% Vinyl
2.

100% Nylon
Padding 100% Cotton
Made in Malaysia
Machine wash. Gentle cycle.
Use mild detergent. Do not
use bleach. Tumble dry low.
Do not twist or wring.

3.

MASON'S
100% Cotton—Preshrunk
MADE IN U.S.A

4.

SPORT CLUB
100% Cotton—Sanforized
MADE IN ITALY

4.

SANA
100% Cotton—Hand Wash
MADE IN HONG KONG

4.

3. Mrs. Lee is going shopping and her husband is doing the wash. She explains what to do, especially with this jacket. What are the things that Mr. Lee should not do? _____

_____

_____

4. Which shirt shrinks the most after washing? _____

_____

Which shirt shrinks the least? _____

_____

Which are imported? _____

_____

Which is the American company? _____

_____

5. Trong washes his red shirt, which is not colorfast, with his white undershirts. What happens? _____

_____

6. Jenny wants to play tennis instead of ironing her husband's shirts. What kind of shirts does she buy for him? _____

_____

B. Department Store Directory

Appliances	Lower Level	Men's	1st Floor
Cosmetics	3rd Floor	Personnel	2nd Floor
Offices	2nd Floor	Shoes	1st Floor
Furniture	4th Floor	Stationery	1st Floor
Kitchenware	Lower Level	Toys	3rd Floor
Jewelry	3rd Floor	TV-Radio	2nd Floor
Linen	2nd Floor	Women's	2nd Floor
Children's	4th Floor	Books	1st Floor
Sporting Goods	Lower Level	Restrooms	2nd Floor

Exercise L-2: Look at the different departments listed above of a department store. Then answer the questions of where someone can find the particular items asked about.

Example: Where can I find makeup? Go to <u>Cosmetics</u> on the <u>3rd</u> <u>floor</u>.

1. Where can I find perfume?

   That's in _____ on the _____ floor.

2. Where can I look at sofas?

   Go to _____ on the _____ floor.

3. Where are the towels?

   They're in _____ on the _____ floor.

4. Do you know where frying pans are?

   Sure, they're in _____ on the _____ .

5. I want to get a doll.

   They're in _____ on the _____ floor.

6. Where can I explain a mistake I have on my bill?

   That is in the _____ on the _____ floor.

7. Where can I find a birthday card?

   _____

8. I want to buy some clothes for a ten-year-old girl.

   _____

9. Where can I pick up a job application?

   _____

10. Where are refrigerators?

    _____

11. I'm looking for a certain best-seller.

    _____

12. Where do you have boots?

    _____

13. _____?

    They're in Women's on the second floor.

14. _____?

    They're in TV-Radio on the second floor.

15. _____?

    Go to the Men's department on the first floor.

31

**DELBERT'S
TV's
*SALE!***

Pay as little as $20 a month!!!
Now through the 15th
All Delbert stores except Concord.

JZR 13″ Color Remote
reg. $350.00 / sale $300.00

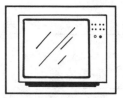

Langer 19″ Color
reg. $369.00 / sale $275.00

C. Comparison Shopping

Exercise L-3: Read the advertisements on the left and answer the following questions about them.

1. How long does this sale last?_____

   _____

2. What are the savings on each TV during this sale? _____

   _____

3. Describe the differences between the two TVs. _____

   _____

4. Which store in the Delbert chain doesn't offer this sale?_____

   _____

5. What does "Pay as little as $20 a month" mean? _____

   _____

D. Warranties

WARRANTY

Full one year warranty on radio with tape player. For one year from the date of purchase, Jetson's will repair this radio with tape player free of charge if defective in material or workmanship. This warranty covers normal consumer use. A purchase receipt or other proof of date of original consumer purchase will be required before warranty performance is rendered.

Vocabulary

warranty—It is the guarantee from the seller to the buyer that the product is what it says it is.

date of purchase—It is the day that the customer buys the product.

free of charge—The customer doesn't have to pay for something.

defective—A product has a defect or something wrong.

workmanship—This is how the product is made.

covers—is responsible for

normal consumer use—The buyer uses the product in a regular way. It has not been accidentally dropped or otherwise abused.

receipt—paper proof of purchase

proof—something that shows it is true

warranty performance is rendered—Consumer gets back money or new product.

Exercise L-4: Answer the questions about the warranty on page 32.

1. For how long is the warranty? _____

_____

2. If you drop this radio and it breaks, will this store pay for

fixing it? _____

_____

3. What do you need to bring when you want to use this warranty?

_____

4. Is this warranty fair? Do all products have them?_____

_____

IX. Problem Solving

Mr. Carson has a full-time job and often comes home late, while Mrs. Carson has part-time work and takes care of their home the rest of the time. They have three children who spend a lot of time after school watching television. The programs they watch have many advertisements. The children are always bothering their mother about getting the new toys they see on television. Mrs. Carson feels bad about this but doesn't know what to do.

A. What is the problem? _____

_____

_____

_____

B. What are all the possible solutions? _____

_____

_____

_____

C. Which solution do you think is best?_____

_____

_____

_____

UNIT 2

FOOD

There is an expression that people often use, "You are what you eat." Eating the right food is important for our health. In this unit we will look at what we eat (nutrition), what kind of food we buy (the supermarket), where we sometimes eat (the restaurant), and how we prepare our food (recipes). The more we know about food, the healthier our lives can be. Welcome to the wonderful world of food!

Objectives

Competencies:
Supermarket Shopping List
Food Labels
Comparison Shopping
Recipes
Menu

Structure
Personal and Indefinite Pronouns
Past and Past Continuous Verbs

Pronunciation:
short i (ĭ)
short i (ĭ) / long e (ē)
TH / T and TH / D

I. Vocabulary

Nutrients
a. vitamins
b. carbohydrates
c. fats
d. proteins
e. minerals
f. water

Fruits & Vegetables	Grain (Bread & Cereal)
Milk Products	Beans, Nuts, Meat & Fish

**Four Food Groups
of a Balanced Diet**

A. Nutrition

1. appetite
2. digestion
3. indigestion
4. staple
5. additives
6. preservatives
7. natural
8. organic
9. vegetarian
10. swallow
11. bite
12. chew

B. Supermarket

1. grocery store
2. shopping basket
3. list
4. coupons
5. aisle
6. shelf
7. produce
8. dairy products
9. unit price
10. butcher
11. delicatessen
12. counter
13. cash register
14. checkout, check out
15. express line
16. bag

C. Recipe

1. ingredient
2. cook
3. fry
4. boil
5. stew
6. simmer
7. steam
8. bake
9. roast
10. grill
11. marinate
12. bread
13. skin
14. dissolve
15. chop
16. mince
17. peel
18. mash
19. shred
20. grate
21. beat
22. sift
23. stir
24. stuff
25. blend
26. whip

D. Restaurant

1. meal
2. buffet
3. feast
4. waiter
5. waitress
6. busboy
7. course
8. dish
9. serving
10. portion
11. helping
12. minimum order
13. menu
14. hors d'oeurve
15. appetizer
16. soup du jour
17. main course
18. entree
19. a la carte
20. dessert
21. beverage

II. Getting Started

A.

B.

Look at both pictures at the left and follow the directions below.

Picture A
1. Describe what's in the picture.
2. Name some good and bad things about eating here.
3. Are there restaurants like these in your native country?

Picture B
1. Describe what's in the picture.
2. Name some good and bad things about eating here.
3. Are there restaurants like this in your native country? What kind of food do they usually serve?

Picture A and B
1. Describe those things that are the same in both pictures and those things that are different.
2. Mr. and Mrs. Tron were planning to go out to dinner when their two-year-old son started acting very badly. Everyone is tired and they are also on a tight budget. Mrs. Tron doesn't like fast food places in the United States, but her husband and son do. Where should they eat?

III. Conversation

A.

1. Did you read the labels while you were buying things at the supermarket yesterday?
2. No. I always seem to be in a hurry. I buy whatever I need and usually what's at the cheapest price.

1. You don't sound too careful.
2. Look, I don't have time to read every little thing on a can or package.

1. Labels can provide you with a lot of valuable information. You can check out the ingredients, the nutrition value, directions for use, and the weight.
2. Does it really make that much of a difference?

1. You are what you eat.
2. Maybe I'll check out the labels next time I go grocery shopping.

B.

1. I'm so worried.
2. What's up?

1. The only thing my son wants to eat is junk food.
2. Junk food?

1. Yes, hamburgers, hot dogs, french fries, ice cream, and things like that.
2. That's a big problem with young people. They like fast food but they end up not getting a balanced diet.

1. Last week as I was serving a nice dinner of fish and vegetables, he got up and left the table. He won't even look at anything green.
2. That's too bad. And you have such a nice garden, too. Well, keep on trying.

1. Well, maybe one of these days he'll change.
2. Between the TV commercials and his friends, sometimes it takes a little time for things to make sense.

C.

1. I went to the new restaurant on Elm Street last night.
2. How was it?

1. The food was great but the service was terrible. They were making mistakes all night.
2. Was it pretty expensive?

1. The prices weren't bad, about moderate. The atmosphere is fabulous: nice plants, stylish furniture, and a beautiful view.
2. Maybe I'll take my mother there when she comes to town next week.

1. She'll probably like it. The service has to get better with time. Everyone was complaining last night.
2. My mom always cooks for herself at home because she's on a strict budget. It's a real treat for her to eat out.

1. There are plenty of items on the menu. And you'd better make reservations if it's Saturday.
2. Thanks, I'll remember that.

Dialogue Puzzle: With a partner fill in the appropriate responses or questions in the spaces of the dialogue below, then practice and read to the rest of the class.

1. What did your friend make for dinner last Wednesday?
2. _____

1. How was it?
2. _____

1. _____
2. She was working all day on it. It was a lot of work.

37

1. _____
2. She learned the recipe from her mother.
1. Which part of the meal did you like the best?
2. _____

_____

Discussion: Answer the following questions about things talked about in the previous conversations.

A. Do you read labels on food you buy? What things are important to look for?

B. Describe a restaurant that you went to.

C. What are the main differences in eating habits between here and your native country? What are the differences in preparing food?

IV. Reading

A. Vocabulary

groceries	grate	aisle	embarrassed
remaining	hum	bargains	relieved
total up	items	ingredients	go through
realize	chop	dish	checkout counter

B. Reading

Maria Gomez is from Colombia in South America. Now she's staying in the United States with her sister, who is married to an American engineer.

Last Monday Maria's brother-in-law invited his boss over for dinner, and so her sister began to go through their mother's old recipe book, looking for a special Colombian dish. After they decided on the menu, Maria rode her sister's bike to the local supermarket to buy a few remaining ingredients. When she got there, she immediately locked her bike to a pole, went in, and grabbed a shopping basket. As she was going down each aisle looking for bargains and the things she needed, she noticed that many items were on sale. She was humming to the music that was playing while she bought a lot of groceries.

When she brought everything to the checkout counter, and the cashier totaled up the bill, Maria realized that she didn't have enough money! She was really embarrassed. She didn't know what to do. Luckily, however, her sister's neighbor was also waiting in line and noticed the problem. She tapped Maria on the shoulder and lent her the necessary money. Maria was quite relieved. She thanked the neighbor and said she would pay her back as soon as she got home.

Maria went outside and put the groceries in the bicycle's basket and also in her backpack. She quickly pedaled home. When she arrived there, her sister was frying chicken, chopping onions, and grating some cheese. Maria didn't want to bother her sister so she kept quiet for a while and quietly unpacked the groceries.

C. Exercises

1. Write these sentences in the correct time sequence of the story, using a 1 for what came first all the way to 7 as last.

_____ a. Maria secured her bike.

_____ b. The neighbor helped out.

_____ c. Maria arrived in the United States from Colombia.

_____ d. The cashier added up the bill.

_____ e. Maria felt embarrassed.

_____ f. Maria's sister looked for recipes.

_____ g. Maria's brother-in-law's boss accepted his dinner invitation.

2. Write *true* or *false*.

_____ a. Maria married an American engineer.

_____ b. Maria rode her sister's bike to the nearby market.

_____ c. The supermarket didn't have anything on sale.

_____ d. Maria enjoyed the music while she was shopping.

_____ e. Maria was arrogant when she realized that she didn't have enough money.

_____ f. When Maria got home, her brother-in-law was cooking.

3. Vocabulary: Put the vocabulary words from Section A (page 38) in the blank spaces.

   a. The butcher can _____ that meat into small pieces.

   b. After shopping at the supermarket, he took the _____ home.

   c. Can you _____ your native country's national anthem?

   d. Did she already _____ the cheese?

   e. My friends always _____ magazines looking for coupons to cut out.

   f. He will _____ the bill again to see if there was a mistake while the cashier was putting everything in a bag.

   g. There are some good _____ at the store this week.

   h. You can read the list of _____ on the side of the package.

   i. He was very _____ when he spilled coffee on her white dress.

   j. She was _____ to know that she didn't have a serious illness.

39

k. Bob was noticing that there were only a few _____ _____ on the list when the store announced it would close.

l. The bride walked nervously down the _____ of the church.

m. He left his keys on the _____ in the store.

n. Do you _____ how late it is?

o. She's preparing a special _____ from her native country for the dinner.

V. Structure

| Pronouns |

A pronoun is a word that takes the place of a noun. We use pronouns so that we don't repeat using nouns. The sentences below show how strange oral and written language can sound if we don't use pronouns.

> The students talked to Mrs. Kesey. <u>She</u> told <u>them</u> that <u>she</u> was busy correcting <u>their</u> exams.

The following sounds much better with pronouns.

> The students talked to Mrs. Kesey. <u>She</u> told <u>them</u> that <u>she</u> was busy correcting <u>their</u> exams.

Here are some more examples of using pronouns.

> Mary looked for the ingredients. <u>She</u> finally found <u>them</u>.

> Bob took his girlfriend to the restaurant but <u>they</u> didn't enjoy the meal.

The pronoun <u>she</u> refers to noun <u>Mary</u>, the pronoun <u>them</u> to the noun <u>ingredients</u>, and the pronoun <u>they</u> to the nouns <u>Bob</u> and his <u>girlfriend</u>.

| Personal Pronouns |

These pronouns name something particularly.

1. Subject pronouns are the subject of a sentence.

	1st Person	2nd Person	3rd Person
Singular:	I	you	he, she, it
Plural:	we	you	they

Object pronouns are the object of the sentence.

	1st Person	2nd Person	3rd Person
Singular:	me	you	him, her, it
Plural:	us	you	them

40

Exercise S-1: Rewrite this paragraph changing the underlined nouns to the correct subject or object personal pronouns.

Karen was talking to Ann and Jim about a new recipe. Karen told <u>Anne</u> and <u>Jim</u> that <u>Karen</u> found <u>the recipe</u> in a magazine. <u>Karen</u> tried <u>the recipe</u> for dinner last week and her guests really liked <u>the recipe</u>.

_____

_____

_____

_____

2. Possessive pronouns are pronouns that show possession.

	<u>1st</u> Person	<u>2nd</u> Person	<u>3rd</u> Person
Singular:	mine	yours	his, hers, its
Plural:	ours	yours	theirs

Example: That is Tim's dish and this is <u>mine</u>.

Possessive adjectives show possession, too, but they go before a noun.

	<u>1st</u> Person	<u>2nd</u> Person	<u>3rd</u> Person
Singular:	my	your	his, her, its
Plural:	our	your	their

In the example above, we can change <u>Tim's</u> to <u>his.</u>

That is <u>his</u> dish and this is mine.

Note the difference between the possessive pronouns and possessive adjectives. The adjective must go before a noun while the pronoun is by itself.

This is <u>my</u> entree and that is <u>yours</u>.

Exercise S-2: Underline the correct answer, the possessive pronoun or the possessive adjective.

    a. This is (my, mine) frying pan and that is (your, yours).

    b. (Our, Ours) kitchen is similar to (their, theirs).

    c. Where is the recipe that you said was (your, yours)?

    d. I enjoyed (her, hers) talk on nutrition despite (your, yours) complaints.

3. Reflexive pronouns are pronouns that refer back to the subject.

    I went there by <u>myself</u>.

The reflexive pronoun <u>myself</u> refers to the subject <u>I</u>.

	1st <u>Person</u>	2nd <u>Person</u>	3rd <u>Person</u>
Singular:	myself	yourself	himself, herself, itself
Plural:	ourselves	yourselves	themselves

Exercise S-3: Use the correct reflexive pronoun in the spaces.

a. I cut _____ very badly with that new kitchen knife.

b. Did you hurt _____ while you were playing?

c. He doesn't know how to take care of _____ .

d. They only think of _____ and not of others. They're selfish.

Review exercise S-4: Now fill in the spaces with the correct personal pronouns. The numbers below each space correspond to the numbers of the kinds of personal pronouns: (1) subject, (2) object, (3) reflexive, (4) possesive or possessive adjective.

Bob looked at _____ watch and realized how late
                      (4)
_____ was. _____ and _____ sister had to buy a
    (1)   (1)   (4)
birthday present for _____ mother. Every year _____
                             (4)   (1)
buy _____ a nice gift. Then Bob's sister said, "_____
         (2)   (1)
don't feel well. _____ think _____'ll stay at home and
                         (1)   (1)
_____ go by _____." Bob agreed and started to leave.
    (1)   (3)
_____ sister held up _____ wallet and asked, "Is
    (4)   (4)
this _____ wallet?" Bob smiled and answered, "Yes, that's
         (4)
_____ . _____ can't go very far without that!"
    (4)   (1)

Review exercise S-5: Now fill in the spaces with the different kinds of personal pronouns without the previous help.

Gary and _____ girlfriend Paula decided to cook a meal

for _____ friends Jim and Kelly, who were celebrating

_____ fifth wedding anniversary. _____ was a surprise

party and _____ planned to have a five-course meal. Gary

prepared the appetizers, a minestrone soup and a salad by

_____ while Paula took care of the main course, baked chicken,

and the dessert, strawberry pie. _____ worked very hard until

_____ was almost time. Gary said to Paula, "_____ have

something very special to tell _____ . Since _____ work

42

very well together, would you like to marry _____ ?" Paula stopped peeling the potatoes and looked at _____ in disbelief. "Are _____ kidding?" _____ asked _____ . Gary smiled and took out a beautiful ring from _____ pocket and put _____ on _____ finger. As the couple was kissing, the doorbell rang.

Indefinite Pronouns

Indefinite pronouns are pronouns that refer to names or things generally, not particularly.

He and his family went to the restaurant. (particular)

Everyone in the family went there. (general)

1. Any, Some

any, anybody, anyone, anything
some, somebody, someone, something

In most cases, some is used for statements and any is used with the negative and with questions.

Somebody is waiting for you outside.
I didn't see anything in that purse.
Did you talk to anyone while you were there?

Some is used in questions when we expect an affirmative answer, or when we want people to say yes.

Could I have some more salad, please?
Do you have some sugar I can borrow?

Exercise S-6: Put in the correct form of some or any in the spaces.

1. He didn't marinate _____ .

2. She wants _____ of those coupons.

3. Did you see _____ that you knew there?

2. Negative

none, no one, nobody, nothing, neither

Do not use two negatives in one sentence.

Incorrect: I don't like nothing here.

Correct: I like nothing here. or I don't like anything here.

Exercise S-7: Use an appropriate negative indefinite pronoun in the spaces.

1. _____ is waiting in the express line now.

2. _____ of his friends visited me.

3. There's _____ in his refrigerator.

4. Ice cream or cake? _____ sounds very good right now.

The other indefinite pronouns most often used are:

all	everybody	most
another	everyone	one
both	everything	one another
each	few	other(s)
each other	many	several
either	more	

Exercise S-8: Underline the indefinite pronoun:

1. While everyone was waiting, Jerry ate all of the cake.

2. Both of them like each other.

3. Few came today but everybody was here yesterday.

4. If you want another, there are more in the cabinet.

5. Chocolate or vanilla? Either is fine.

6. The students are talking with one another. Several are in the classroom. The others are outside.

Exercise S-9: Write the correct indefinite pronoun in the space.

1. _____ of the children had their vitamins.
   a. Anything   b. All   c. Something

2. Excuse me, but do you have _____ napkins?
   a. any   b. no one   c. something

3. Yes, there are _____ on aisle seven.
   a. any   b. no one   c. some

4. Was _____ at the diet center?
   a. anybody   b. few   c. some

5. Those dishes are unique. _____ is hand-painted.
   a. Both   b. Each   c. Few

6. Do you want chocolate or vanilla ice cream? _____ is fine.
   a. Nobody   b. Several   c. Either

7. _____ came. It was quite crowded.
   a. Many   b. Anybody   c. One

8. Where did the students go? There are _____ in class.
   a. one   b. everybody   c. few

9. He was very hungry. He ate _____ on his plate.
   a. anybody   b. everything   c. no one

10. Those two stores are always competing with _____ .
    a. other   b. each other   c. any

11. Where is _____ ?
    a. everybody   b. somebody   c. both

Past and Past Continuous Verbs

A. Past

Regular

I cooked	I didn't cook	Did I cook?
You cooked	You didn't cook	Did you cook?
We cooked	We didn't cook	Did we cook?
They cooked	They didn't cook	Did they cook?
He cooked	He didn't cook	Did he cook?
She cooked	She didn't cook	Did she cook?
It cooked	It didn't cook	Did it cook?

Irregular

I began	I didn't begin	Did I begin?
You began	You didn't begin	Did you begin?
We began	We didn't begin	Did we begin?
They began	They didn't begin	Did they begin?
He began	He didn't begin	Did he begin?
She began	She didn't begin	Did she begin?
It began	It didn't begin	Did it begin?

Verbs in the past tense describe a definite past action (indicated by such words as <u>yesterday, last week, three years ago.</u>)

Last month her husband cleaned the house.

Short answers: Did he feel well? Yes, <u>he did.</u> or No, <u>he didn't.</u>

Exercise S-10: Write the correct past form of the verbs in parentheses.

Example: (invite) When <u>did</u> she <u>invite</u> the dinner guests?

1. (marinate) _____ you _____ the meat?
   Yes, I _____ it in white wine then.

2. (spoil) _____ the milk _____ overnight?
   (Short answer) No, _____ .

45

3. (sift) How thoroughly _____ he _____ the flour?

He _____ it several times.

4. (bring) _____ the waiter _____ them appetizers?

Yes, he _____ them a few minutes ago.

5. (stuff) _____ the cook _____ the turkey?

Yes, she _____ it with fruit and rice.

6. (need) What _____ the supermarket _____?

It _____ a greater variety of cheeses.

(Negative) It surely _____ _____ more vegetables.

7. (beat) How long _____ she _____ the eggs?

She _____ them as long as the recipe said to.

8. (stick) _____ the cheese _____ to the casserole dish?

(Short answer) Unfortunately _____ .

9. (take) _____ the vegetarian _____ only small portions?

(Short answer) Yes, _____ .

10. (check) Are you sure that she _____ the unit prices?

(Short answer) Yes, I'm positive that _____ .

B. Past Continuous

I was cooking	I wasn't cooking	Was I cooking?
You were cooking	You weren't cooking	Were you cooking?
We were cooking	We weren't cooking	Were we cooking?
They were cooking	They weren't cooking	Were they cooking?
He was cooking	He wasn't cooking	Was he cooking?
She was cooking	She wasn't cooking	Was she cooking?
It was cooking	It wasn't cooking	Was it cooking?

Verbs in the past continuous tense describe an action in the past, sometimes over a longer amount of time.

They <u>were studying</u> from nine until twelve o'clock.

Many times you can use either the past or past continuous to describe a past action.

She <u>studied</u> hard yesterday.

She <u>was studying</u> hard yesterday.

Short answers: Was he peeling the potatoes?

Yes, <u>he was</u>. or No, <u>he wasn't</u>.

Were they steaming the vegetables?

Yes, <u>they were.</u> or No, <u>they weren't</u>.

Exercise S-11: Write the correct forms of the <u>past</u> <u>continuous</u> in the spaces.

1. (cut) Were they _____ out coupons all morning?

   Yes, they _____ them out of magazines.

2. (munch) _____ he _____ on popcorn throughout the movie?

   (Short answer) Yes, _____ .

3. (help) How long _____ she _____ you?

   She _____ me for two hours last week.

4. (drag) Why _____ he _____ his feet?

   (not-eat) Because he _____ a balanced diet.

5. (total up) _____ the grocery clerk _____ the figures?

   (Short answer) No, _____ . (stack) _____ cans.

6. (write) _____ she _____ a romantic letter to her boyfriend when her mother opened the door?

   Yes, she _____ a very romantic letter when her mother surprised her.

The past and the past continuous tenses are often in the same sentence. The past continuous describes a past action in progress when the past action happens. Note the use of <u>when</u> and <u>while</u> in these examples.

When his parents arrived, he was sleeping.
While they were talking, the teacher entered the classroom.
We were baking bread when the accident happened.
Bob called while his brother was doing his homework.

Exercise S-12: Change the verbs in parentheses to their proper tenses.

1. When the guests _____ ,
   (arrive—past)

   the host _____ .
   (cook—past continuous)

2. While the potatoes _____ ,
   (boil—past continuous)

   Mary _____ a magazine.
   (read—past)

3. I _____ when he _____ .
   (sleep—past continuous)   (call—past)

4. The vegetables _____ when
   (steam-past continuous)

   the phone _____ .
   (ring-past)

47

Exercise S-13: Now form your own sentences with the past and past continuous, using the same forms as above.

1. When _____ , _____ .
           (Past)   (Past Continuous)

2. While _____ , _____ .
       (Past Continuous)   (Past)

3. _____ when _____ .
   (Past Continuous)   (Past)

4. _____ while _____ .
   (Past)   (Past Continuous)

VI. Composition

Write your own words in the blanks, following the indications below in parentheses. After you finish, let your teacher correct and then read aloud to the class.

I live _____ blocks from a supermarket. I go there
      (how many)

_____ . The item that I buy most often is
  (how often)

_____ . Last _____ , while I
 (name of food)   (time)

_____ in this supermarket, I _____ .
 (past continuous)   (past)

In my native country when I was young I liked to eat

_____ because _____ . My
  (food)   (reason you liked it)

favorite meal was _____ , which was prepared
      (name foods in the meal)

by _____ . A very unusual food of my native country
 (person)

that you don't find here is _____ .
        (food)

When it's real cold I like to eat _____ , while in
        (food)

hot weather I prefer _____ . The food that I don't care
    (food)

for is _____ . The healthiest food that I can
   (food)

recommend is _____ . People in the United States
    (food)

seem to eat a lot of _____ .
    (food)

I _____ go to a restaurant. My favorite one
  (how often)

is _____ , located in _____ . I like it
 (name of restaurant)   (city)

because _____ .
      (reason you like it)

VII. Pronunciation

A. Vowel:

short i (ĭ)

1. kitchen
   grill
   simmer

2. nutrition
   mince
   minimum

3. additives.
   sift
   skin

4. Their bill is still on the list near the dishes.

5. He had indigestion after dinner.

Contrasts: Short i (ĭ) / long e (ē)

6. mitt/meat
   fist/feast
   live/leave

7. bin/bean
   did/deed
   lick/leak

8. list/least
   lip/leap
   whip/weep

B. Consonants:

TH / T and TH / D

1. thigh/tie
   thought/taught
   threw/true

2. bath/bat
   both/boat
   math/mat

3. then/den
   those/doze
   death/dead

4. They thought the bathroom had thin walls.

5. The teacher taught both those themes.

VIII. Life Skills

A. Supermarket Shopping List

Exercise L-1: Here is your shopping list for your trip to the supermarket. Write down the item below the aisle heading where you would most likely find it.

butter	tissues	chunk light tuna	ginger ale
oregano	diet cola	oatmeal	carrots
marmalade	lettuce	cranberry juice	cantaloupe
fresh shrimp	yogurt	furniture polish	olives
swiss cheese	cake	whole wheat bread	napkins
egg noodles	jellybeans	can of pinto beans	spaghetti
toilet paper	rice	salad dressing	brown sugar
rubber gloves	mouthwash	ground chuck	mineral water
frozen vegetables	deodorant	saltine crackers	vegetable oil
TV dinner	cornflakes	frozen orange juice	peanut butter
pork chops	fig bar cookies	toothpaste	air freshener
rolls			

1 Dairy Products

_____
_____
_____

2 Beverages

_____
_____
_____

3 Produce

_____
_____
_____

4 Macaroni & Rice	5 Health Care	6 Cereals & Sugar
_____	_____	_____
_____	_____	_____
7 Household Needs	8 Canned Goods	9 Oil, Salad Dressing & Spices
_____	_____	_____
_____	_____	_____
10 Frozen Food	11 Meat & Fish	12 Jams, Juices & Peanut Butter
_____	_____	_____
_____	_____	_____
13 Baked Goods	14 Paper Products	15 Candy, Cookies & Crackers
_____	_____	_____
_____	_____	_____
_____	_____	_____

B. Food Labels

1. JACKSON'S

CONDENSED

2. TOMATO SOUP

3. NET WT. 10¾ OZ. (305 GRAMS)

4. JACKSON SOUP CO.
LOS ANGELES, CALIF.

5.	CONDENSED	WITH MILK
PROTEIN	2	10
VITAMIN A	8	10
VITAMIN C	40	40
THIAMINE	*	2
RIBOFLAVIN	*	10
NIACIN	4	4
CALCIUM	*	10
IRON	2	2

* CONTAINS LESS THAN 2% OF THE
US RDA OF THESE NUTRIENTS

6. INGREDIENTS: TOMATOES, CORN SYRUP, WHEAT FLOUR, SALT, PARTIALLY HYDROGENATED VEGETABLE OIL (SOYBEAN OR COTTONSEED OIL), NATURAL FLAVORING, ASCORBIC ACID (VITAMIN C) AND CITRIC ACID.

7. NUTRITION INFORMATION PER SERVING

SERVING SIZE   4 OZ (CONDENSED)
(8 OZ AS PREPARED—226 G)

SERVINGS PER CONTAINER   2¾

	CONDENSED	WITH MILK
CALORIES	90	160
PROTEIN (Grams)	1	5
TOTAL CARBO-HYDRATES (G)		
Simple Sugars (G)	10	15
Complex Carbo-hydrates	7	7
FAT (G)	2	6
SODIUM	750 mg/serving	810

PERCENTAGE OF US RECOMMENDED
DAILY ALLOWANCES (US RDA)

8. DIRECTIONS: In pan, bring soup and 1 can of water to simmer. Stir. For Cream of Tomato, use milk instead.

Information

1. Name of company (brand name)
2. Name of product
3. The weight of the product (inside)

4. Name and place of manufacturer, distributor or packer
5. Health information about the product (how the body will use the soup)
6. The materials in the product (what's in the soup)
7. Additional health information about the product
8. Directions (how to prepare the soup)

Exercise L-2: Answer the following questions about the soup label.

1. What should you add before you heat the soup?_____
   _____

2. Mr. Arlington is on a salt-free diet. Should he eat this soup? Why?
   _____

3. Bob is cooking dinner for his girlfriend. Is this enough soup for them? Explain. _____
   _____

4. Joan really wants to lose weight. Which is better for her, according to the number of calories—a couple of slices of cheddar cheese at 230 calories or a serving of Jackson's tomato soup? ____
   _____

5. Is this soup a significant source of Vitamin C? _____
   Explain._____

6. Is the net weight the weight of the can plus the food or the food only?
   _____
   What is the weight of only the soup? _____

7. The unit price labels you sometimes see on shelves help you compare prices. Which soup below actually costs less per weight?
   _____

UNIT PRICE **3¢** PER OUNCE	YOU PAY **35¢**	UNIT PRICE **3.2¢** PER OUNCE	YOU PAY **34¢**
Zesty-O Soup 11.67 oz.		**Jackson's Soup 10.5 oz.**	

8. Explain the meaning of the following words that you see on products and give examples of which kinds of products have them.

   Refrigerate After Opening: _____
   Keep Frozen:_____

Add Egg:_____

Buy Before Jan. 12:_____

Perishable: _____

C. Comparative Shopping

Exercise L-3: Read the following advertisements from the two markets and then answer the questions that follow.

Bob's Market	**Sunset Market**
Ground Chuck $1.89 lb. "Incomparable!"	Ground Beef $ .98 lb. Does not exceed 30% fat.
Dixie Napkins 140 Count $ .79	Softie Napkins $1.89 Family Pack, 360 Ct. Save 20 cents
Apples 4 lbs. $ .99 California Grown, Sweet, Juicy Pippins and Golden Delicious	Jonathan Apples $ .39 lb. Crisp and full of juice!
D and T Sugar from Hawaii 5 lb. pak $1.59	D and T Sugar $1.49 5 lb. bag
Mertson's Ketchup 32 oz. Bottle $1.39	El Mar Catsup 44 oz. $1.99
Bell Tuna Chunk Light, 6.5 oz. $ .59 Save up to 20 cents!	Chunk Tuna Captain John's $ .69 Water or Oil 6½ oz.

1. What are the differences between the two hamburger meats at the two markets?_____

_____

2. Which napkins are cheaper per napkin? _____

_____

3. Which store has the better deal on apples? Explain. _____

_____

4. What's the difference between the two markets' sugar sales?

_____

5. Which ketchup/catsup is a better buy? Explain. _____

_____

6. What are the differences between the two stores' tunas?_____

_____

7. You bought 2 lbs. of apples, 4 cans of tuna, and 5 lbs. of ground chuck at Bob's Market. How much change would you get back if you paid with a twenty dollar bill? _____

8. Jerry bought a bottle of ketchup, 5 lbs. of sugar, and three cans of tuna at Sunset Market and his friend Jose bought the same items at Bob's Market. Who had a smaller bill? _____

_____

D. Recipes

Exercise L-4: Read the following recipe and then answer the questions that follow.

Pancakes

3 teaspoons baking powder
1 tablespoon sugar
1¼ cups sifted flour
½ teaspoon salt

1 beaten egg
1 cup of milk
2 tablespoons salad oil or melted shortening

Sift the baking powder, the sugar, the flour, and the salt together. In another bowl put the egg, milk and salad oil; add to dry ingredients, stirring just until the flour is a little wet. The batter will be lumpy.

Bake on a hot griddle. Makes about 12 small-sized pancakes or 6 average-sized ones. For variety, add different fruit to the batter.

1. Write in the ingredients measured with these measuring spoons and indicate how many are used.

   Tablespoon   Teaspoon   ½ Teaspoon

   _____   _____   _____

2. What do you do with all the dry ingredients first? _____

   _____

3. What do you do with the egg, milk and salad oil after they are put together in a bowl? _____

   _____

4. Fill in the cups of how much is used.   Flour   Milk

5. Where do you bake the pancakes? _____

   _____

6. Jason is making a surprise breakfast for his mother, father, and sister. Will he have enough pancakes to serve if he follows this recipe? Explain. _____

   _____

7. Mary told Barbara to add some crushed apple to the batter for a change. Was that a good idea? Why? _____

   _____

53

E. Menu

Exercise L-5: Read the menu and then answer the questions that follow.

Welcome to # SUSAN'S RESTAURANT

Dinners are served daily from 5 to 10 P.M.
(Closed Mondays)

Appetizers

Shrimp Cocktail	$1.75
Fruit Plate	1.50
Chicken Wings	2.00
Paté	2.75

Soups

	cup	bowl
Clam Chowder	$1.00	$1.75
Onion	.80	1.35
Soup Du Jour	.95	1.45

Salads

Tossed Green	$ .75
Salad Bar	2.89

Beverages

Coffee	$ .40
Tea	.40
Milk	.35
Soft Drinks	.50

Dinners include soup or salad, two vegetables, french bread and butter,
brown rice or baked potato or french fries, and dessert.

Entrees	A la Carte	Dinner
Baked Chicken	$5.95	$7.95
Sirloin Steak	6.95	9.95
Fillet of Sole	5.95	7.95
Prime Rib	7.95	10.95
Roast Beef	5.95	7.95
Pork Chops	5.95	7.95
Prawns	7.95	10.95

<u>Desserts:</u> Sherbet .80, Ice Cream .75, Pie 1.00

Mimimum Service $2.50   **Ask our waitress about the Special of the Day**

---

1. When is this restaurant open? Could Mr. Wu stop there after work on Tuesday night about 8:30? _____

   _____

2. If Susan ordered a glass of wine with her roast beef dinner, what would the waitress say? _____

   _____

3. Henry ordered a bowl of onion soup, a fillet of sole dinner, and some sherbet with a cup of tea. Margaret had a shrimp cocktail, a tossed green salad, and a prawn dinner with coffee. Who had the higher bill? _____

   _____

4. What's the difference between a la carte and dinner? _____

_____

5. If Miss Harrison orders just a bowl of the soup du jour for dinner, what will the waitress say? _____

_____

6. What's the most expensive item on the menu?_____

_____

7. How do I find out about the special of the day? _____

_____

8. Glenda says, "With a salad bar, that's enough for me, especially after all those dinner parties I went to." Why does she say this?

_____

_____

9. Mr. Henderson's family went to Susan's restaurant. This is what they had: Mr. Henderson, pork chop dinner with coffee; Mrs. Henderson, chicken wings and a sirloin steak dinner with a cola; Barbara Henderson, prime rib a la carte, apple pie and milk.

Is their bill correct?

_____

How much of a tip will they probably leave?

_____

Susan's Restaurant	BILL
Date _____ No. _____	
Table _____ Server _____	
chicken wings	2.00
pork chop dinner	7.95
steak dinner	9.95
prime ribs a la carte	10.95
apple pie	1.00
milk	.35
coffee	.40
cola	.50
TAX	
TOTAL	33.10

IX. Problem Solving

Mr. Crosby is a middle-aged salesman who has a lot of stress in his job. He just got a divorce. The doctor told him that he is overweight and must lose 20 pounds and get on a sensible diet. Mr. Crosby usually eats in fast-food restaurants or buys frozen dinners which he can quickly prepare and eat in front of the TV. He hates to go shopping at a supermarket because he says the lines are always too long. A friend at work recommended diet pills for his weight problem, and another gave him the address of a weight control center. What is your advice?

A. What is the problem? _____
_____
_____
_____

B. What are all the possible solutions? _____
_____
_____
_____

C. What solution do you think is best? _____
_____
_____
_____

UNIT 3

HEALTH

"If you have your health, you have everything," the wise grandfather tells his grandchildren. In so many ways he's right. For a new person in this country, understanding health is necessary. We must be able to describe symptoms, understand prescriptions, and follow medical procedures. When completed, several sections in this unit can be used as reference information to help in a time of medical need.

Objectives

Competencies:
Immunizations
Health Services
Doctor's Questionnaire
Medical History
Medicine Labels

Structure
Subject and Verb Agreement
Future and Future Continuous Verbs

Pronunciation:
long a (ā)
long a (ā) / short e (ĕ)
TH / Z and TH / S

I. Vocabulary

A. Medical

1. patient
2. nurse
3. receptionist
4. hospital/clinic
5. appointment
6. medical history
7. checkup/medical/physical exam
8. diagnosis/diagnose
9. symptom
10. run a test
11. blood test/draw blood
12. stool sample
13. urine test
14. eyesight/vision (20/20)
15. hearing/deafness
16. blood pressure
17. pulse
18. take the temperature
19. thermometer
20. reflexes
21. look after/care for/take care of/tend
22. cure/remedy
23. recover/recuperate/get well
24. injection/shot/immunization/vaccination
25. chart
26. pap test/cervical smear
27. saliva
28. mucus
29. blood type
30. intravenous feeding (IV)
31. autopsy
32. stethoscope
33. needle/syringe
34. bandage
35. cast
36. operation/operate on

B. Conditions

1. in good health/healthy
2. condition (good, stable, grave)
3. sickness/illness
4. disease
5. trouble/problem/disorder
6. disability/handicap
7. hygiene
8. suffer from
9. faint/pass out
10. fainting/dizzy spells
11. nausea
12. sneeze/catch a cold
13. cough
14. wheeze
15. pneumonia
16. bronchitis/asthma
17. tuberculosis (TB)
18. vomit/throw up
19. choke
20. inflammation/swelling
21. pain/hurt/injury/injure
22. severe/acute/sharp
23. chronic
24. ache (back, tooth, ear, head, stomach)
25. migraine
26. ulcer
27. cramp
28. allergy
29. hay fever
30. wound
31. cut
32. scratch
33. bruise
34. concussion
35. fracture/broken
36. sprain
37. fever/high temperature/chill
38. constipation
39. diarrhea
40. vitamin deficiency
41. infection
42. contagious
43. congestion
44. indigestion/heartburn/upset stomach
45. rash
46. anemia
47. shock
48. heart attack/cardiac arrest
49. stroke
50. high blood pressure
51. epilepsy/seizure
52. coma
53. hemorrhage
54. athlete's foot
55. insomnia
56. flu/virus
57. sore throat/strep throat
58. kidney stones
59. varicose veins
60. tumor
61. miscarriage
62. abortion
63. whooping cough
64. diptheria
65. chicken pox
66. measles
67. mumps
68. appendicitis
69. addiction
70. arthritis
71. cancer
72. cataract
73. glaucoma
74. clotting
75. diabetes

C. Body

1. throat
2. lungs
3. heart
4. liver
5. stomach
6. kidneys
7. intestines
8. bladder

D. Remedy

1. prescription
2. medication
3. medicine
4. dose
5. pill
6. tablet
7. capsule
8. lozenge
9. ointment
10. aspirin
11. antibiotic
12. pain-killer/analgesic
13. sedative/tranquilizer
14. sleeping pill
15. valium
16. laxative
17. over-the-counter
18. stimulant
19. codeine
20. morphine
21. contraceptive
22. suppository

E. Drug Awareness

1. upper/downer
2. amphetamine
3. cocaine/crack
4. speed
5. heroin
6. PCB
7. marijuana

F. Doctors

1. M.D./physician
2. general practitioner
3. surgeon (surgery)
4. intern
5. neurologist (neurology)
   nervous system
6. cardiologist (cardiology)
   heart
7. urologist (urology)
   urine and urinary organs
8. internist (internal
   medicine)
9. ophthalmologist/oculist
   (opthalmology)
   eye and its diseases
10. optometrist (optometry)
    testing vision and
    fitting of glasses
11. ear, nose, eye and throat
    specialist
12. orthopedist (orthopedics)
    muscles and bones
13. dermatologist(dermatology)
    skin
14. dietitian (dietetics)
    diet and nutrition
15. radiologist (radiology)
    x-ray
16. podiatrist (podiatry)
    feet
17. pathologist (pathology)
18. dentist (dentistry)
19. pediatrician (pediatrics)
    children
20. obstetrician (obstetrics)
    pregnancy and labor
21. gynecologist (gynecology)
    women
22. industrial medicine
    specialist
23. psychologist (psychology)
    mind, mental and
    emotional processes
24. psychiatrist (psychiatry)
    study, treatment and
    prevention of disorders
    of the mind
25. anesthesiologist
    (anesthesiology)
26. chiropractor
27. veterinarian

II. Getting Started

A.

B.

Picture A

1. Describe what's in the picture.
2. When do you use this hospital entrance?
3. What are the entrance procedures to hospitals in your native country?

Picture B

1. Describe what's in the picture.
2. When do you use this hospital entrance?
3. What are the emergency entrance procedures in your native country?

Pictures A and B

1. Point out the similarities and differences.
2. Mr. Gomez's son falls off his bike and hits his head and loses consciousness. What should he do?

III. Conversation

A.

1. Do you know a good doctor that I can go to?
2. Yes, our family doctor is excellent, but he charges a little more than other doctors. Do you have medical insurance?

1. No, I don't, but if he's a good doctor, then I don't care what he charges.
2. What seems to be your problem?

1. I have this recurring pain in my side.
2. Well, it's best not to take any chances. You never know what you might have. Here is our doctor's name and phone number.

1. Thank you. I'll give him a ring right away. I hope it isn't anything serious though.
2. Don't worry, you'll be in good hands with this doctor.

B.

P = Patient   D = Doctor

P: I always feel down, as if I don't have enough energy.

D: What's your diet like?

P: I'm always on the go, so I eat a lot in restaurants and fast food places, hamburgers, hot dogs, french fries, whatever's easiest.

D: It sounds as if you've got a junk food diet. You know, your body needs foods that provide lots of vitamins.

P: Will you explain that?

D: Vegetables, greens and fruits, for example.

P: No, I don't eat those very often.

D: Well, try to make them part of your diet. Also, get a proper amount of rest each night.

P: Yes, I really went to bed late all last month with that report I had to do for my job.

D: Take care of yourself, read this brochure about nutrition, and I think you'll be just fine.

P: Thanks a lot, Doctor.

C.

GS = Grandson   GP = Grandpa

GS: Grandpa, why don't you ever want to go to the doctor?

GP: Ah, what does a doctor know that I don't know?

GS: You mean you don't trust them?

GP: If you ask me, they all get paid too much money, and they're always worrying about malpractice suits and their new machines and wonder drugs.

GS: They don't seem to be that bad to me. I know a few who are very dedicated.

GP: I'm sure there are a few. What gets me is that they try to find something wrong with you when they know you're perfectly well.

GS: What are you going to do then?

GP: I'm just going to take care of myself, eat right, do enough exercise, and not worry about things.

Dialogue Puzzle: With a partner fill in the appropriate responses or questions in the spaces below, then practice and read to the rest of the class.

1. _____

2. I'm not feeling very well.

1. _____

2. I have a sore throat, swollen glands, and a very high temperature.

1. Maybe it's the flu. I hear that it's going around.

2. _____

1. You look very pale. You really should go see a doctor.

2. _____

1. _____

2. That's good advice.

1. _____

2. Thanks a lot. See you later.

Discussion: Answer the following questions about things you talked about in the previous conversations.

1. What was wrong the last time you didn't feel well?
2. What was the worst injury that ever happened in your family?
3. How many kinds of specialist doctors have you or a family member or a friend visited?
4. What are common medicines in your native country? Is there a difference between over-the-counter and prescription drugs in your native country?

IV. Reading

A. Vocabulary

chicken pox	panic	get the chance
particular	do business	get in touch with
arrange	pass out	take in the sights
surgical	annual	are supposed to
relieved	ambulance	
prone	misunderstand	

B. Reading

Last year Sabine's mother said to her family, "I can hardly wait—soon we will be leaving for the United States for Father's annual business trip." But that never happened. Sabine's brother broke his leg after falling from a tree. And the year before that she had the chicken pox. The family seemed to be accident prone, but this year they got another chance to leave Switzerland and they took it.

After they settled in and her father arranged his business matters in surgical supplies, Sabine, her mother, and her brother studied English and took in all the sights of the area where they were staying.

One day their bad luck returned. As they were going out for a ride, Sabine's mother slipped and fell on a wet part of the sidewalk in front of their house. She remained there crying out in pain, "Oh, no, it's probably my disc!"

"I'll call for help," Sabine said as her mother passed out. Sabine tried not to panic. She ran into the house and called her father but the line was busy.

Then she called the 911 emergency number. She was very nervous about using her English. "I don't know what to do," she explained. "My mother fell on the pavement and she's hurt."

The operator asked, "Do you want me to get you in touch with a particular hospital?"

Sabine answered, "We're new here and we don't know any doctors or hospitals—I just don't want to see my mother like this. Will you get an ambulance? We're at 311 Elm Street."

The operator replied, "Sure, don't worry, one's on the way right now."

Sabine went back outside and was relieved to see her mother awake, sitting up and talking to her brother. It was not as serious as she at first believed.

The ambulance arrived and one of the paramedics asked, "Where's the pregnant woman?"

Sabine was confused but then realized her mistake. She explained, "I said that my mother fell on the pavement—it wasn't the word 'pregnant'—I guess you misunderstood me!"

They all laughed and then Sabine's mother said, "I feel much better, and even more knowing that I'm not going to have another baby!"

C. Exercises

1. Write these sentences in the correct time sequence of the story, using a 1 for what came first, all the way to 7 as last.

   _____ a. Sabine called for professional help.

   _____ b. The ambulance pulled up in front of the house.

   _____ c. Sabine's brother broke his leg.

   _____ d. Her mother lost consciousness.

   _____ e. Sabine got the chicken pox.

   _____ f. The operator sent the ambulance.

   _____ g. Sabine's mother slipped and fell.

2. Write *true* or *false*.

   _____ a. Sabine's father dealt in hospital equipment.

   _____ b. Sabine talked with her father right after her mother's accident.

   _____ c. Sabine was very confident in her English.

   _____ d. The operator was helpful.

   _____ e. The ambulance driver was looking for a pregnant woman.

   _____ f. Her mother was seriously hurt.

   _____ g. This family came from Europe.

3. Put the vocabulary words from Section A (page 62) in the spaces.

   a. _____ is usually a childhood disease.

   b. Please _____ my cousin when you're in Detroit. Here is his phone number. Give him a ring.

   c. "It was a pleasure to _____ with you," said one salesman to the other.

63

d. Your friend is always getting hurt. He's really accident _____ .

e. The surgeon examined all the new _____ instruments.

f. At the _____ meeting they will _____ the new financial reports.

g. You _____ be there by seven or the boss will get mad.

h. The student was _____ that the teacher didn't _____ what he was trying to say.

i. We ought to _____ a nice going-away party for him.

j. If you _____ when you're in New York, _____ and go to a Broadway show.

k. She's very _____ about what she eats. She's very hard to please.

l. The _____ is really well equipped for any kind of emergency.

m. "Don't _____ . You have plenty of time."

V. Structure

Subject and Verb Agreement

A. The verb must agree with its subject in person (I, you, he, they, etc.) and number (singular or plural).

Clint gets a checkup every year.
  S   V

They are paying the high bill.
 S   V

Two subjects joined by and are called compound subjects and they are plural.

The doctor and I are going over my medical history.
    S   V

B. These pronouns are singular: everyone, everybody, everything, someone, somebody, something, no one, nobody, each, another, one, neither, and either.

Nobody is waiting in line.
Something is wrong with that machine.
Each boy and girl has an immunization card.
Either thermometer is fine.

These pronouns are singular or plural, depending on the meaning:
all, more, most, some, and enough.

> All the medicine is on the tray.
>
> All the pills are in the bottle.
>
> Some of the criticism was unfair.
>
> Some of the nurses want longer breaks.

C. The subject follows the verb to be in the sentences beginning with there and here.

> There were two operations at the hospital this morning.
>   V   S

D. When two subjects are joined by either-or or neither-nor, the verb agrees with the subject closer to it.

> Either my aunt or my cousins are coming over.
>   S   S   V
>
> Neither you nor I am driving there.
>   S   S V

E. Words joined to a subject by with, in addition to, along with, together with, except, as well as or other prepositional phrases don't affect the verb.

> Mr. Chen, along with his family, is going to the clinic.
>   S   V
>
> The working schedule of the surgeons is ready.
>   S   V

F. An expression of quantity or extent (pounds, kilograms, miles, years, dollars, etc.) takes a singular verb if the amount is considered as a unit, and takes a plural verb when the amount is considered as a number of individual units.

> Thirty pounds is too much to lose in a month.
>   S (unit)   V (singular)
>
> Thirty pounds of different kinds of grains are enough.
>   S (individual units)   V (plural)

Exercise S-1: Underline the correct word in parentheses.

1. Either of the antibiotics (is/are) sufficient.
2. The question of medical insurance (seem/seems) to confuse a lot of people.
3. The class in drug awareness (meet/meets) every Monday at one o'clock.
4. Either Mrs. Gibson or one of her secretaries (know/knows).
5. Money, as well as credit and references, (is/are) necessary.
6. Everyone at the hospital (has/have) done a great job.
7. A hundred dollars (is/are) a lot to pay for a checkup.
8. There (was/were) many mistakes in her bill.
9. Neither you nor I (are/am) interested in going.
10. All of their health problems (is/are) the result of vitamin deficiency.

11. Exercise and a good diet (is/are) necessary.
12. Not one of all those reports (has/have) what I want.
13. The receptionists as well as the manager (deserve/deserves) the praise.
14. Four days (is/are) a long time to wait for the results.
15. His favorite breakfast (is/are) bacon and eggs.
16. In addition to his report, his diagnosis (was/were) superb.
17. The list of hospital regulations (is/are) not available right now.
18. Somebody (want/wants) to talk to you.
19. Each of the women usually (arrive/arrives) before ten.
20. The whole problem, together with the other reports, (has/have) nothing to do with the Robinson case.

Finish these sentences with an appropriate verb that agrees with the subject.

1. Mrs. Johnson, along with her children, _____ .
2. Nobody in the operating room _____ .
3. Some of the patients _____ .
4. Either my cousins or my uncle _____ .
5. Every one of my symptoms _____ .
6. Two hundred dollars _____ .
7. Neither the doctor nor the nurses _____ .
8. The hospital _____ .
9. Not one of those kids _____ .
10. Cancer, as well as heart attacks, _____ .

Future and Future Continuous Verbs

A. Future

1.

I will help	I will not help	Will I help?
You will help	You will not help	Will you help?
We will help	We will not help	Will we help?
They will help	They will not help	Will they help?
He will help	He will not help	Will he help?
She will help	She will not help	Will she help?
It will help	It will not help	Will it help?

2.

I'm going to try	I'm not going to try	Am I going to try?
You're going to try	You aren't going to try	Are you going to try?
We're going to try	We aren't going to try	Are we going to try?
They're going to try	They aren't going to try	Are they going to try?
He's going to try	He isn't going to try	Is he going to try?
She's going to try	She isn't going to try	Is she going to try?
It's going to try	It isn't going to try	Is it going to try?

Verbs in the future tense describe a future action. The two above forms of writing the future are the same.

> I will leave next week.
> I'm going to leave next week.

Contractions: will = 'll / will not = won't

> She'll be here tomorrow.
> They won't get here until seven.

Short answers: (1) Will he write the letter this Saturday?
Yes, he will. or No, he won't.

(2) Is she going to drop by this afternoon?
Yes, she is. or No, she isn't.

Exercise S-2: Write the correct form of the future in the spaces, using form (1) with the odd numbers and form (2) with the even ones.

Example: (take) <u>Will</u> she have to <u>take</u> medicine every day?
Yes, she <u>will</u>.

1. (keep) _____ they _____ the clinic open till six?
Yes, they _____ it open till at least that.

2. (sprain) _____ he _____ his weak ankle in the game? Yes, I think that he _____ it.

3. (bill) _____ they _____ us next month? No, they _____ us until the end of the year.

4. (complain) _____ your friend _____ about the medicine? No, he _____ about it.

5. (operate) _____ the doctor _____ on your friend? Yes, _____ . (Short answer)

6. (catch) _____ she _____ a cold? Yes, _____ . (Short answer)

7. (faint) _____ the new nurse _____ at the sight of blood? No, _____ . (Short answer)

8. (keep) _____ the accounting office _____ track of all their bills? Yes, it _____ track of all financial transactions.

9. (take care) _____ Larry _____ of himself after he leaves the hospital? Yes, I hope he _____ . (Short answer)

10. (borrow) _____ your mother-in-law _____ from you again? No, it's just the opposite: I _____ _____ from her.

B. Future Continuous

I will be returning	I won't be returning
You will be returning	You won't be returning
We will be returning	We won't be returning
They will be returning	They won't be returning
He will be returning	He won't be returning
She will be returning	She won't be returning
It will be returning	It won't be returning

Will I be returning?
Will you be returning?
Will we be returning?
Will they be returning?
Will he be returning?
Will she be returning?
Will it be returning?

Verbs in the future continuous tense describe a future action that is in progress or going on.

She'll be working in emergency all morning tomorrow.

This form can also be used with the form of the verb be + going to.

She's going to be working in emergency all morning tomorrow.

They're going to be arriving soon.

Short answers: Will you be working then?
Yes, I will. or No, I won't.

Exercise S-3: Write in the correct form of the future continuous verb.

Example: (travel) <u>Will</u> the patient <u>be</u> <u>traveling</u> in a car? No, he <u>will</u> <u>be</u> <u>traveling</u> in a private ambulance.

1. (take care of) _____ that nurse _____

   my son? Yes, she _____ him all this week.

2. (suffer) _____ you _____ from hay

   fever there? No, I _____ from it there.

3. (deal) _____ the neurologist _____

   with people she doesn't know? No, she _____ .

   (Short answer) They'll all be old patients.

4. (take) _____ he _____ her pulse

   this afternoon? Yes, he _____ . (Short answer)

5. (help) _____ the dietitian _____

   you? Yes, she _____ as soon as she is free.

Use <u>be</u> + <u>going</u> <u>to</u> form.

6. (talk) _____ you _____
to the doctor before the end of the week? Yes, I _____
_____ to her about my arthritis.

Exercise S-4: Answer these questions with future or future continuous verbs.

1. What will you be doing tomorrow night?

   _____

2. When are you going to see your friend?

   _____

3. Where will you spend your next vacation?

   _____

4. How will you be getting home today?

   _____

5. Why are you going to be leaving early?

   _____

Exercise S-5: Write your own sentences using the verbs and tenses in parentheses.

1. (Future—get)_____

   _____

2. (Future Continuous—take care of)_____

   _____

3. (Future—change)_____

   _____

VI. Composition

Exercise C-1: Write words of your choice according to the descriptions below each space. After you finish, let your teacher correct and then read aloud to the class.

Medical care in the United States is _____ .
(adjective)

The hospitals are _____ , the nurses are
(adjective)

_____ and the doctors are _____ .
(adjective)   (adjective)

The best thing about hospitals here is _____
(sentence)

_____ . A big health problem here is _____

_____ .
(name of health problem)

69

The difference between medical care in my native country and the

United States is that _____
(sentence)

_____ . The biggest health problem there

is _____ .
(name of health problem)

Modern medicine has many advantages and disadvantages. One

advantage is _____ while a disadvantage is
(noun)

_____ . I _____ to stay healthy.
(noun)   (future verb)

Modern medicine _____
(future continuous verb)

in the future.

VII. Pronunciation

A. Vowel:

long a ($\bar{a}$)

1. faint	2. spray	3. operation
patient	migraine	stable
contagious	ache	they

4. The remaining eighteen stayed and ate late.

5. They paid for the vaccinations in May.

Contrast: long a ($\bar{a}$) / short e ($\breve{e}$)

6. sail/sell	7. bait/bet	8. raid/red
gate/get	main/men	taste/test
tale/tell	fade/fed	paste/pest

B. Consonants:

TH / Z and TH / S

1. think/zinc	2. thank/sank
breathes/breezes	thing/sing
clothe/close	faith/face
teething/teasing	worth/worse

3. They think they'll close the zinc mine.

4. It's worth it to use the zip code.

VIII. Life Skills

A. Immunizations

All children need protection against the diseases of polio, diptheria, tetanus, whooping cough (pertussis), rubella (german measles), and the mumps. Check your health records to make sure your children have received all their immunizations.

Immunizations Recommended by the American Academy of Pediatrics

Disease	No. of Doses	Age for 1st Series	Booster
Diptheria Tetanus Whooping Cough (DPT)	4	2 months 4 months 6 months 18 months	At 4 to 6 years before entering school. As recommended by doctor.
Polio (oral vaccine)	4	Same as above	Same as above
Measles	1	1 to 12 years	None
Mumps	1	1 to 12 years	None
Rubella	1	After 1 year	None
*Recommendations change from time to time as science gains new knowledge.			

Exercise L-1:

1. How many diseases are listed here?_____

2. Which vaccine is taken by mouth?_____

3. Which diseases only need 1 vaccination? _____

4. How many shots does a child get in total for DPT? _____

5. Children have a natural immunity (protection) to many diseases. When are they in danger with rubella?_____

   _____

6. Why can't a child receive the four DPT doses at one time? _____

   _____

7. When might this chart change?_____

   _____

8. What place would require these immunizations? _____

   _____

71

B. Health Services

Exercise L-2: Find the names and addresses and phone numbers in a directory or other information source for this health services list.

1. Information Numbers

   Public Library:

   _____   _____

   Health Department:

   _____   _____

   Hospitals:

   _____   _____

   Other:

   _____   _____

2. Health Services

   Community Health Clinic:

   _____   _____

   Children's Health Services:

   _____   _____

   Crisis or Family Counseling:

   _____   _____

3. Special Health Services

   Heart Disease Organization:

   _____   _____

   Cancer Organization:

   _____   _____

   Alcohol Abuse Center:

   _____   _____

   Drug Abuse Center:

   _____   _____

   VD Clinic:

   _____   _____

   Family Planning Service:

   _____   _____

4. Hotlines

   Parent Stress _____ Suicide Prevention _____

   Crisis _____ Other _____

Exercise L-3: Read the following situations and recommend one of the above places to contact.

1. Mr. X has been drinking heavily for the past two months, ever since he got laid off from work. He's very depressed and withdrawn.

   _____

2. Y sniffs cocaine before she goes to the disco every weekend. Now she feels that she needs it also during the week. She's not happy.

   _____

3. Z's children are going to school but she must get immunizations for them.

   _____

4. X's husband beats her up quite often.

   _____

5. W says he doesn't want to live anymore.

   _____

6. What do you think is the biggest health problem in your community now?

   _____

C. Doctor's Questionnaire

Exercise L-4: Go over this questionnaire to see how you would answer each question.

Fitness and Health Protection

YES	NO
☐	☐	1. Are you doing the most to keep yourself healthy?
☐	☐	2. Do you feel that your diet is balanced?
☐	☐	3. Have you had a complete physical checkup in the last three years?
☐	☐	4. If over 40, did the checkup include an eye test for glaucoma?
☐	☐	5. Do you exercise regularly?
☐	☐	6. If overweight, are you reducing?
☐	☐	7. If over 40 and male, do you limit intake of solid fats and dairy products?
☐	☐	8. Are you familiar with the signs of cancer?
☐	☐	9. If over 25 and female, have you had a smear taken from your uterus for examination in the last year and have you learned to examine your breasts for lumps?
☐	☐	10. Have you stopped or reduced smoking?

Immunization

11. Have you been vaccinated against:

YES	NO
☐	☐	—Polio, in the last 5 years?
☐	☐	—Tetanus-diptheria, a booster dose in the last 5 years?
☐	☐	—Measles, if you haven't had them?
☐	☐	—Smallpox, every 3 years (especially if you travel)?
☐	☐	—Typhoid, every 5 years (if travel)?
☐	☐	—Influenza, every year if over 65 or have heart or lung disease?

Automobile Safety

YES	NO
☐	☐	12. Do you use seat belts in your car?

Emotional Health

YES	NO
☐	☐	13. Do you talk about emotional or social problems (family problems, depression, insomnia, worries, alcohol/drug abuse) with your doctor when the need arises?

D. Medical History

Exercise L-5: Go over the following medical history form to see how you would fill it out.

HAVE YOU HAD ANY PROBLEMS WITH: (Check)

Past Illnesses		Diseases	
Frequent colds	———	Measles	———
Sore throats	———	Chicken pox	———
Bronchitis	———	Mumps	———
Allergies	———	Scarlet fever	———
Operations	———	Polio	———
Serious injuries	———	Whooping cough	———
Upset stomach	———	Other:	
Convulsions	———	_____	———
Kidney trouble	———	_____	———
Tuberculosis	———		
Diabetes	———		

Blood Diseases		Immunizations-Tests	
Anemia	———	Diptheria	———
High blood pressure	———	Whooping cough	———
Heart attacks	———	Polio	———
Mental depression	———	Tetanus	———
Bad headaches or		Small pox	———
migraines	———	Typhoid	———
Liver trouble		Tuberculin	———
(hepatitis)	———	Other:	
		_____	

List the medications you are now taking:

_____

Allergies to medications:

_____

Surgeries/Dates:

_____

E. Medicine Labels

There are two kinds of medicine: 1) over-the-counter, which anyone can buy, and 2) prescription, which a doctor must order in writing.

<u>Over-the-Counter</u>

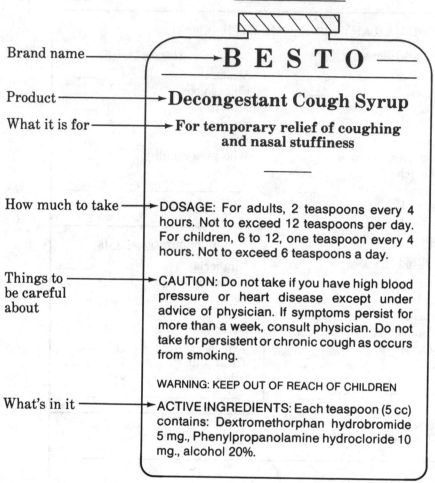

Brand name —— **B E S T O**

Product —→ **Decongestant Cough Syrup**

What it is for —→ **For temporary relief of coughing and nasal stuffiness**

How much to take —→ DOSAGE: For adults, 2 teaspoons every 4 hours. Not to exceed 12 teaspoons per day. For children, 6 to 12, one teaspoon every 4 hours. Not to exceed 6 teaspoons a day.

Things to be careful about —→ CAUTION: Do not take if you have high blood pressure or heart disease except under advice of physician. If symptoms persist for more than a week, consult physician. Do not take for persistent or chronic cough as occurs from smoking.

WARNING: KEEP OUT OF REACH OF CHILDREN

What's in it —→ ACTIVE INGREDIENTS: Each teaspoon (5 cc) contains: Dextromethorphan hydrobromide 5 mg., Phenylpropanolamine hydrocloride 10 mg., alcohol 20%.

<u>Prescription</u>

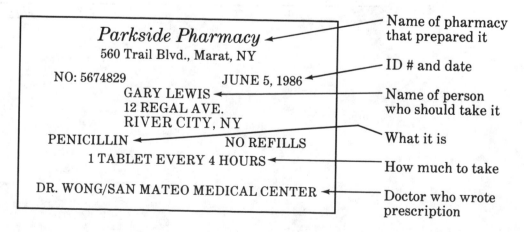

Parkside Pharmacy ←—— Name of pharmacy that prepared it

560 Trail Blvd., Marat, NY

NO: 5674829   JUNE 5, 1986 ←—— ID # and date

GARY LEWIS ←—— Name of person who should take it
12 REGAL AVE.
RIVER CITY, NY

PENICILLIN ←   NO REFILLS   What it is

1 TABLET EVERY 4 HOURS ←—— How much to take

DR. WONG/SAN MATEO MEDICAL CENTER ←—— Doctor who wrote prescription

Exercise L-6: Answer these questions about the above medicine labels.

1. Where can you buy BESTO cough syrup? Who can buy it?_____

_____

2. How many teaspoons of BESTO does an adult take in 12 hours?

_____

3. Can Johnny, a 10-year-old, take 2 teaspoons of cough syrup every 8

hours? _____

4. What symptoms is a decongestant good for? _____

_____

5. Which person below can take BESTO without asking a doctor?

_____

  —Mr. Nick Carter who is a heavy smoker and has a smoker's cough
  —Mrs. Benson who has been taking BESTO for 10 days
  —Henry Smith who has a cough and stuffed-up nose
  —Doris Quin who has high blood pressure

6. Does BESTO contain alcohol? _____

7. Where is Parkside Pharmacy located? _____

_____

8. Gary Lewis took a penicillin pill at 4:00 in the afternoon. When

should he take the next tablet? _____

9. When Gary runs out of tablets, can he get more? _____

10. Where does Dr. Wong work? _____

_____

SMITH'S FIRST AID SPRAY

For cuts, scratches, insect bites, minor burns, sunburn. Helps prevent infection and relieves pain and itching.

DIRECTIONS: Hold 3 to 6 inches away and spray injured area.

WARNING: Use only as directed. Avoid spraying in eyes, mouth, ears and on other sensitive areas of the body.

Exercise L-7: Answer these questions about Smith's First Aid Spray.

1. Is this an over-the-counter drug or prescription? _____

_____

2. What are the precautions?_____

_____

3. Who should use this? _____

_____

  —John who stayed out in the sun too long at the beach
  —Mary who cut herself with a knife
  —Chuck who got mosquito bites

IX. Problem Solving

Susan's husband fell down while carrying a heavy box at his job and hurt his back. He asked his boss if he could go home and the boss said OK. He returned home and gradually felt worse and worse. After a while he said that the pain was too strong. Then he passed out. What should Susan do?

1. What is the problem? _____

_____

_____

2. What are all the possible solutions? _____

_____

_____

3. Which solution do you think is best?_____

_____

_____

_____

UNIT 4

TELEPHONE

One of the most common places to speak English is on the telephone. This isn't always so easy as it appears. We only hear the voice and don't see the person who is speaking, so we have to be sure that we are listening well. In this unit we will examine those vital aspects of using English on the telephone.

Objectives

Competencies:
Pay Telephone
White Pages
Yellow Pages
Messages
Long Distance Rates

Structure
Adjectives, Comparisons and Suffixes
Imperative Verb Form
Helping Verbs: May, Might, Can, Could, Should, Ought To, Had Better, Must, Have To, Be Supposed To, Used To

Pronunciation:
short e (ĕ)
short e (ĕ) / long a (ā)
F / P and B / P

I. Vocabulary

A. Telephone Vocabulary

1. telephone (phone)
   a. receiver
   b. cord
   c. receiver button
   d. hook
   e. dial
2. dial tone
3. busy signal
4. number
5. prefix
6. area code
7. directory (phone book)
8. white pages/listing
9. yellow pages
10. government listings
11. unlisted (unpublished) number
12. emergency numbers
13. toll free/800 number
14. rates
15. phone booth/public phone
16. coin/slot
17. extension
18. installation/install
19. call/make a call/ring/ call up/give a ring (buzz)/ phone
20. billing inquiries
21. answering machine
22. answering service
23. phone service
24. hearing impaired
25. telecommunications
26. wrong number
27. sales call
28. abusive, harassing, threatening or obscene calls

II. Getting Started

A.

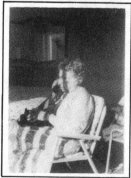

B.

Picture A

1. Describe what's in the picture.
2. What are the advantages and disadvantages of using this kind of phone?
3. How do pay phones here compare to those in your native country?

Picture B

1. Describe what's in the picture.
2. What are the advantages and disadvantages of using this kind of phone?
3. How does phone service here compare with that in your native country?

Pictures A and B

1. Describe those things that are the same in both pictures and those things that are different.
2. Jose has been waiting a long time to use the pay phone. It's an important call to his boss. There's a teenage girl on the phone and she is chewing gum and laughing a lot. There don't seem to be any phones nearby. What should Jose do?

III. Conversation

A.

1. Hello, is Bob there?
2. No, he isn't. Can I take a message?

1. Yes. Tell him that John Catson called.
2. Would you mind repeating that?

1. Here, let me spell it for you: J-O-H-N C-A-T-S-O-N. Got that?
2. Fine. Let me read it back to you. I hope I didn't make a mistake. J-O-H-N C-A-T-S-O-N.

1. That's right. Tell him that it's urgent.
2. Urgent?

1. Yes, it's very important. And remind him not to use my old number. He got the wrong number the last time he called.
2. I'll make sure that he gets the message as soon as he comes in.

B.

1. Operator, I'd like to make a long distance call to Spokane, Washington.
2. Will that be a person-to-person call?

1. No, I'll talk to anyone who answers.
2. Then you can just dial that number directly. You don't need operator assistance.

1. Really? Is it cheaper that way?
2. Yes, it is. Just dial the area code and the regular number.

1. What do I do if I want to know how much it costs?
2. Then you need operator assistance. Just ask for the time and charge.

1. Could you explain that a little more?
2. After your call, the operator will ring you and tell you how long you talked and how much it was.

1. That sounds like a useful thing to know. Thank you for your help.
2. You're welcome.

C.

1. I called my brother long distance last night, and the reception was terrible. I could barely hear him.
2. Did you do anything about it?

1. What do you mean?

2. Well, if you have a bad connection on the phone, you can hang up and call the operator and either get another line or else credit for your call.

1. I didn't realize that I could do that.
2. By the way, did you get your directory last week?

1. Yes, and my name was in it.
2. Did they have your correct address and phone?

1. Yes, everything was perfect.
2. Sometimes people don't want to have their name and phone in public so they get an unlisted number.

1. Is that just for privacy?
2. Yes, I believe so.

Dialogue Puzzle: With a partner fill in the appropriate responses or questions in the spaces of the dialogue below, then practice and read to the rest of the class.

1. _____

2. I found it in the yellow pages.

1. _____

2. There were many listed.

1. Did you call them?

2. _____

1. What did they say?

2. _____

1. _____

2. That seems fair.

1. _____

2. Yes, that was a good deal.

Discussion: Answer the following questions about things talked about in the previous conversations:

1. Who usually answers the phone in your house?
2. How often do you talk on the phone?
3. Who do you usually call?
4. What time of day does your phone ring the most?
5. Who do you have difficulty talking to on the phone?

IV. Reading

A. Vocabulary

receiver	get through	couldn't take it
signal	hang up	motioned
over	giggle	in person
steep	get off	long distance
put down	dial	convince
chip in		

B. Reading

Mr. Giovanni Gotelli arrived from Italy two years ago with his wife, Vanya, and their two children, Sandra and Mario. Giovanni got a job as a mechanic at his brother-in-law's auto service. Both he and Vanya studied English at the adult school in the community. Since the school term was coming to an end, they decided to have a party for their teacher and invite all the students in the class. Giovanni went over the class list and prepared to call each of them. First, though, he waited for his daughter Sandra to get off the phone. He had warned her before about staying on the phone too long because of the steep bills and also in case of an emergency or special long distance call.

Sandra continued talking and giggling with her girlfriend, trying to decide which boy was the most handsome in their classes. Finally Giovanni couldn't take it any longer. He went up to her and motioned his finger from one side of his throat to the other. "Hang up soon," he whispered. Sandra got the message and said good-bye to her friend.

Giovanni dialed the first number on the class list, heard a busy signal, and then tried again a few minutes later. This time he got through.

"Hello."

"Hello, is Juan there?"

"Yes, this is he."

"Oh, Juan, this is Giovanni. Your voice sounds different on the phone. Do you have a cold?"

"No, but I hate to speak English on the phone. I prefer to speak to someone in person."

"Juan, I had to call you to invite you to our class party on Saturday at my house. Everyone is bringing a dish that is typical of his or her native country, and we're all chipping in for a gift for our teacher. Do you think you can make it?"

"Sure, but I don't know how to cook. Maybe I can convince my girlfriend to make something special."

"Well, be sure to invite her also."

"Good enough. We'll be there. And I'll bring some money for the gift. Thanks for the invitation."

"Bye."

Giovanni put down the receiver and looked up to see Sandra waiting for another chance to get back on the phone.

83

C. Exercises

1. Write these sentences in the correct sequence of the story, using a 1 for what came first, all the way to 7 as last.

_____ a. Sandra called her friend.

_____ b. Giovanni indicated that he wanted Sandra to stop talking.

_____ c. Giovanni and his family arrived in the United States.

_____ d. Juan said that he would bring some money for the gift.

_____ e. Giovanni heard a busy signal.

_____ f. Juan answered the phone.

_____ g. Giovanni and Vanya decided to have a party.

2. Write *true* or *false*.

_____ a. Sandra was discussing serious matters with her friend.

_____ b. Giovanni's family sometimes got long distance calls.

_____ c. Sandra always obeyed her father.

_____ d. Giovanni had a list of his classmates to invite to the party.

_____ e. Juan enjoyed talking on the phone.

_____ f. The class party was on the weekend.

_____ g. The class was still undecided about what gift to get for the teacher.

3. Put the vocabulary words from Section A (page 83) in the spaces.

a. You have to _____ 1 plus 800 for the toll-free number.

b. She will _____ the phone as soon as she gets tired of holding the _____ .

c. Let's _____ and buy a pizza. I think we have enough money.

d. She saw the movie star _____ .

e. During the boxing match he _____ to his friend that he _____ , so they left.

f. They drove _____ 400 miles.

g. The car stopped at the _____ on the _____ hill.

h. The little girls always _____ when they get together.

i. As soon as they _____ the phones, you will be able to _____ with your _____ call.

j. He _____ his pen and rested.

k. Will she ever _____ you to take her to that fancy restaurant?

V. Structure

> **Adjectives**

An adjective is a word that describes a noun or pronoun.

The <u>bright</u> student passed the test. He is <u>happy</u> about it.

The adjective <u>bright</u> describes the noun <u>student</u> and the adjective <u>happy</u> describes the pronoun <u>He.</u> Usually adjectives come before the noun they describe, as in "bright student." Sometimes adjectives come after the noun they describe, usually two in written English and set off by commas.

The telephone operator, <u>tired</u> and <u>exhausted</u>, finally took a break.

The adjectives <u>tired</u> and <u>exhausted</u> describe the noun <u>operator</u>. Adjectives that describe the subject of the sentence and not the action of the verb come after these special verbs: <u>be, seem, appear, become;</u> and verbs of the senses: <u>smell, taste, feel, sound,</u> and <u>look.</u>

Lunch in the cafeteria smells <u>delicious.</u>
She seems <u>upset.</u>
The supervisor feels <u>fine.</u>
It tastes <u>fantastic.</u>
He appeared <u>serious.</u>
The picture looks <u>great.</u>

Exercise S-1: Fill in the spaces with your own adjectives.

1. The _____ house is on the _____ hill by a _____ park.

2. The _____ mother told her _____ son to clean his _____ room.

3. I talked with the telephone operator. She was _____ .

4. She looked _____ after receiving the obscene phone call.

85

5. It tastes _____ but it doesn't smell

_____ .

6. I am usually _____ after I argue with my friends.

7. Does he feel _____ after the exam?

Comparison of Adjectives

The <u>comparative</u> is used to compare two persons or things. Most adjectives of one syllable add <u>-er;</u> adjectives of more than one syllable add <u>more</u> before.

> Jason is <u>older</u> than Trong.
> Marie is <u>more intelligent</u> than her sister.

If an adjective has one syllable plus a <u>y</u>, change the <u>y</u> to <u>i</u> and add <u>er.</u>

> The office is <u>busier</u> in the morning than the afternoon.

Exercise S-2: Write the correct <u>comparative</u> form of the adjective.

1. (loud) John is _____ on the phone than you.

2. (expensive) It's _____ to call my country than yours.

3. (easy) It's _____ to find a business number in the yellow pages than the white pages.

The <u>superlative</u> is used to compare more than two persons or things. Most adjectives of one syllable add <u>-est;</u> adjectives of more than one syllable add <u>most</u> before.

> He is the <u>shortest</u> one of the three clerks.
> She was the <u>most gracious</u> of all the receptionists.

If an adjective has one syllable plus <u>y</u>, change the <u>y</u> to <u>i</u> and add <u>-est.</u>

> Your friend was the <u>happiest</u> one in the class after she received the call.

Exercise S-3: Write the correct form of the <u>superlative</u> form of the adjective.

1. (bright) The color of that phone is the _____ of all the phones here.

2. (complicated) The phone installation was the _____ thing I have ever seen.

3. (busy) He has the _____ phone in the whole office.

With a few adjectives, both kinds of comparative and superlative forms can be used. These adjectives are: quiet, common, stupid, tired, handsome, polite, pleasant, cruel and adjectives that end in -ow (hollow), -er (clever), and -le (gentle).

It is quieter in this neighborhood than in that one.
It is more quiet in this neighborhood than in that one.

The following adjectives have irregular comparisons:

good	better	best
bad	worse	worst
little	less	least
many	more	most
much	more	most
far	farther	farthest
far	further	furthest

(Farther is used for distance while further is used for the idea of additional, extra or more advanced.)

That city is farther away than this one.
She went further than he did in school.)

Exercise S-4: Write the comparative and superlative of these adjectives.

	Comparative	Superlative
1. flat	_____	_____
2. wise	_____	_____
3. pretty	_____	_____
4. early	_____	_____
5. brilliant	_____	_____
6. thoughtful	_____	_____
7. slippery	_____	_____
8. amazing	_____	_____
9. bad	_____	_____
10. tired	_____	_____

Now practice using the above comparison of adjectives in sentences of your own.

_____

_____

_____

_____

_____

_____

_____

_____

Exercise S-5: Answer the following questions with the comparison of adjectives.

Example: Who is the better dancer, you or your sister?
My sister is better than I am.

1. Who is taller, you or your teacher?

_____

2. What is the name of the largest river in your native country?

_____

3. What is easier for you, to talk on the phone or to listen?

_____

4. What is the most beautiful tourist attraction in the world?

_____

5. Who is sitting the closest to the teacher?

_____

6. What is the most disturbing problem in the world?

_____

7. What was the most spectacular thing that you have ever seen?

_____

8. Who has been the kindest to you?

_____

9. What is the worst kind of weather?

_____

10. Which is more difficult to learn, science or literature?

_____

Exercise S-6: Write the <u>comparison</u> form of the adjectives in parentheses.

1. (good) That was the _____ movie that I saw last year.

2. (cheap) Which of the two phones is _____ ?

3. (serious) Who is _____ , your uncle or your aunt?

4. (careful) She was the _____ person in her family.

5. (sleepy) You look _____ than me.

6. (nice) Bill is _____ than his three brothers.

7. (thin) Jack is the _____ of the three boys.

8. (reliable) Is your answering machine _____ than mine?

9. (bad) The news is just too _____ to discuss.

10. (little) You lent him _____ money than you lent me.

Suffixes: Adjective Endings

These are some common adjective endings, followed by three examples. Change the noun in parentheses to an adjective in each sentence and write it in the blank.

1. -OUS: serious, nervous, tremendous

   (mystery) It was the most _____ place I have ever been.

2. -IVE: cooperative, aggressive, festive

   (information) That was really an _____ TV program.

3. -ISH: foolish, childish, Swedish

   (style) She always wears very _____ clothes.

4. -AL: technical, internal, intellectual

   (grade) It was a slow and _____ change in the temperature.

5. -ABLE: comfortable, enjoyable, portable

   (agree) My friend is an _____ person.

6. -IBLE: edible, visible, terrible

   (horror) The movie that they showed on Halloween was really _____ .

7. -FUL: careful, hopeful, graceful

   (doubt) They were _____ that she was home.

8. -LESS: tasteless, helpless, careless

    (home) After the flood, people were left _____ .

9. -Y: dirty, watery, itchy

    (fault) The plane couldn't take off; it had a _____ engine.

10. -IC: majestic, realistic, acidic

    (tragedy) The play disappointed us with its _____ ending.

Exercise S-7: Match the adjective with its correct ending.

1.	oil	less
2.	joy	ish
3.	inquisit	ible
4.	practic	y
5.	care	ive
6.	wonder	ful
7.	fool	able
8.	respons	ous
9.	lov	al

Now write the complete adjectives from above in the sentences below.

1. Tools are very _____ .
2. The _____ clown made everyone laugh.
3. The _____ boy asked a lot of questions about all the _____ things of nature.
4. The choir sang a _____ song for the festive occasion.
5. You shouldn't be _____ when using knives.
6. Parents must be _____ when they take their children to the swimming pool.
7. Her hair is very _____; she needs a shampoo.
8. The mother always kisses her baby; she's such a _____ child!

Exercise S-8: Use the endings -ous, -ful, or -able to change the underlined words to adjectives.

1. The magazine had a lot of <u>humor.</u> There were quite a few _____ articles in it.

2. He's always <u>forgetting</u> things. He's really _____ .

3. The earthquake was a <u>disaster</u>. The loss of life was really very

_____ .

4. She always calls and <u>cheers</u> me up. She's such a _____

person.

5. The phone company is famous for its <u>courtesy.</u> Every one of their

workers is _____ .

6. Have you tried <u>washing</u> that shirt yet? It says it's machine

_____ .

7. We had little <u>success</u> in learning how to operate the answering

machine. We weren't _____ .

8. I would <u>prefer</u> a different kind of phone. Anything would be

_____ to this one.

The Imperative

The imperative of the verb indicates a command or request. The subject <u>you</u> is not written. It can be plural or singular.

> Turn left on Third Avenue.
> Come on in.
> Stand up and stretch.

The negative of the imperative is <u>Don't</u> plus the present verb.

> Don't yell in the phone.

The imperative that includes the speaker uses <u>Let us,</u> or more common, <u>Let's.</u> The negative is <u>Let's</u> <u>not.</u>

> Let's get out of here.

Many times the imperative is used with polite expressions, the most common being <u>please</u>.

> Please dial the area code first.

Other polite expressions with or without please are <u>will you</u> or <u>would you</u>.

> Will you please have your tickets ready.
> Would you stay to your right, please.

The polite expressions <u>do you mind</u> or <u>would you mind</u> also use the imperative form. Note that these expressions don't have a question mark and are pronounced like sentences. The main verb ends in -ing.

> Do you mind holding on for a minute.
> Would you mind calling back later.

Exercise S-9: Write sentences using the imperative form.

1. (sit)_____
2. (deny-not)_____
3. (write) Let's _____
4. (stay-not) Let's _____
5. (get) Please _____
6. (go) Would you _____
7. (turn) Will you _____
8. (come) Would you mind _____
9. (take) Do you mind _____

Exercise: Write three sentences with the imperative that you would say to a visitor to your home.

1. _____
2. _____
3. _____

| Helping Verbs |

Helping verbs are verbs that come before and help the main verb.

He <u>will</u> come over to your house tomorrow.

They <u>don't</u> know how to make a collect call.

The secretary <u>didn't</u> know where a public phone was.

<u>Will</u> is the helping verb of the future verb in the first example above. The negative forms of <u>don't</u> and <u>didn't</u> are also helping verbs of the present and past tenses. The following are other helping verbs.

A. May/Might

<u>May</u> is to show permission.

You <u>may</u> smoke in that other section.

<u>May</u> is also for a possible future action.

She <u>may</u> call you this afternoon.

In direct speech the past of <u>may</u> is <u>might</u>.

He said he <u>might</u> be late.

Nowadays <u>might</u> is used the same as <u>may</u> when meaning a future possible action.

She <u>may</u> give you a ring tomorrow.

She <u>might</u> give you a ring tomorrow.

For the possibility that past events happened or a past event that was possible but didn't happen, use <u>may</u> or <u>might</u> plus <u>have</u> and the <u>past participle of the verb.</u>

Bob's late. He <u>might</u> <u>have</u> <u>missed</u> the bus.

I had to leave the game early. They <u>may</u> <u>have</u> <u>won.</u>

Her son played too rough with the other kids. He <u>might have hurt</u> one of them. (But he didn't.)

Exercise S-10: Rewrite these sentences using the forms of <u>may</u> or <u>might</u>.

Example: It's possible he will go.
He may go.

1. It is possible that she will have the report ready by noon.

   _____

2. Maybe Mr. Carson will give them an exam.

   _____

3. You have permission to use the phone.

   _____

4. Mary's not here. Possibly she woke up.

   _____

5. The child played by the pool. It was possible for him to have drowned.

   _____

B. Can/Could

We use <u>can</u> to express ability, power or capacity to do something.

He <u>can</u> speak many languages.
Anybody <u>can</u> find out the rates.
The elevator <u>can</u> hold 40 persons.

<u>To be able</u> is the same as <u>can</u> but it is used less.

She <u>is able to</u> do her math all by herself.

In the future, <u>will be able to</u> is used, although <u>can</u> has the same meaning.

They <u>will be able to</u> find the government listings.
They <u>can</u> come next Saturday.

The past of <u>can</u> is <u>could</u> or <u>was/were able to.</u>

When he was young, he <u>could</u> run very fast.

To say someone had the ability to do something in the past but didn't do it, use <u>could</u> plus <u>have</u> and the <u>past participle</u> of the verb.

I <u>could</u> <u>have</u> <u>gotten</u> a discount on that phone last year.

C. Should/Ought To/Had Better

Should, ought to and had better express obligation and duty, advice or an opinion of what is right and correct. Should is used more often.

> You should talk to the operator right away.
> Her father ought to check the telephone bill.
> I'd better leave. It's getting late.

We form the past for should and ought to with have and the past participle of the verb.

> They should have spoken with you sooner.
> He ought to have looked it up in the yellow pages.

D. Must/Have To

We use must or have to to express necessity or strong obligation.

> They must get the emergency phone numbers.
> He has to leave now if he wants to catch the train.

Must doesn't have a past or future form. We use have to for these forms.

> He had to sign the form yesterday.
> She will have to take the test tomorrow.

E. Be Supposed To

Be supposed to refers to what people should do, especially regarding laws and rules, or what is expected to happen.

> You are supposed to send the phone bill by the due date.
> The program was supposed to begin at nine.

F. Used To

Used to describes an action that continued for some time in the past but that doesn't happen at the present time.

> He used to smoke. (Now he doesn't.)
> They used to pay with credit cards. (Now they don't.)

Exercise S-11: Complete the following sentences with your own words. Select from helping verbs in A through F above.

1. I can _____.

2. When my friend was younger, he could _____
   _____.

3. I could have _____.

4. The lost tourist asked the taxi driver, "Could _____
   _____."

5. We must _____.

94

6. They will have to _____

if they want to get there on time.

7. The secretary had to _____

last week.

8. The father should _____ .

9. Everyone ought to _____ .

10. I had better _____ .

11. She prepared such a nice meal for us last night. We should _____

_____

12. The teacher should have _____

last month.

13. The students are supposed to _____ .

14. I was supposed to _____

but I just didn't have the time to do it.

15. My relative used to _____ .

VI. Composition

Exercise C-1: Write words of your choice according to the descriptions below each space. After you finish, let your teacher correct and then read aloud to the class.

The phone service in the United States is _____ .
(adjective)

It is _____ to make a _____
(difficult/easy)   (type of call)

call. Operators are usually _____ . I prefer to
(adjective)

_____ rather than _____ on the
(talk/listen)   (talk/listen)

phone. The worst kind of call to get is _____ , while the
(kind of call)

best kind is _____ . I use the telephone directory when
(kind of call)

I _____ .
(sentence)

If I have a problem on the phone I should _____
(sentence)

_____ . I have _____ phone(s) in my home
(how many)

that (are/is) _____ with a _____
(color)   (kind of dial)

dial. I _____ use the public telephone. The last time I
(how often)

used one was _____ .
(when)

95

The phone service in my native country is _____
_____ (comparative adjective)

_____ than the United States. It's _____
(more/less)

expensive to use the phone in my native country. The operators are

_____ . _____ owns the
(adjective)   (who)

telephone service and operates it. The worst thing about the telephone

there is _____ .
(adjective)

VII. Pronunciation

A. Vowel:

short e (ĕ)

1. pr<u>e</u>face	2. sp<u>e</u>ll	3. t<u>e</u>lephone
dir<u>e</u>ctory	coll<u>e</u>ct	gu<u>e</u>ss
<u>a</u>ny	cr<u>e</u>dit	<u>e</u>dge

4. Their fr<u>ie</u>nds t<u>e</u>sted the emerg<u>e</u>ncy <u>e</u>xits

5. He'll g<u>e</u>t t<u>e</u>n ch<u>e</u>cks on his d<u>e</u>sk by th<u>e</u>n.

Contrast: short e (ĕ) / long a (ā)

6. pen/pane	7. men/main	8. best/baste
pest/paste	wren/rain	wet/wait
fed/fade	bet/bait	ten/tame

B. Consonants: F / P and B / P

1. <u>f</u>act/<u>p</u>acked	2. <u>b</u>an/<u>p</u>an
<u>f</u>aint/<u>p</u>aint	sym<u>b</u>ol/sim<u>p</u>le
cuf<u>f</u>s/ cup<u>s</u>	ro<u>b</u>e/ro<u>p</u>e
chie<u>f</u>/chea<u>p</u>	ri<u>b</u>/ri<u>p</u>

3. The <u>p</u>air <u>f</u>ound a <u>b</u>unch of cup<u>s</u>.

4. His wi<u>f</u>e <u>f</u>ainted and <u>f</u>ell <u>b</u>y the <u>p</u>ail.

VIII. Life Skills   A. Pay Telephone

Western Bell | 20¢ | **5-10-25 U.S. Coins Only**

Local calls, deposit coins before dialing. Other calls see instructions below. Refunds not provided on amounts over-deposited for local calls.

1 Stop
2 Listen for tone
3 Deposit coins

20¢

Coin Release

Lost/stolen calling cards 800-621-0430
Calling Card Calls:
    Within Area . . . . .0 + Number
    Outside Area . . . . 0 + Area Code + Number
Wait for special tone, then dial calling card number.

Cash Calls:
    Within Area . . . . Number
    Outside Area . . . . Area Code + Number

Collect, Person-to-Person, 3rd Number Calls:
    Within Area . . . . .0 + Number
    Outside Area . . . . 0 + Area Code + Number

Operator Assistance:
    Within Area 0
    Outside Area 00
Directory Assistance:
    Within Area 411
    Outside Area . . . . Area Code + 555-1212

PUSH FOR COIN

1. How much does it cost to make a local call?_____

2. Can you use a quarter for a local call? If you do, do you get change back? _____

3. What do you do before inserting the coins? _____

4. If you can't find your calling card, what should you do? _____

_____

5. How do you make a collect call outside of the area code you are in?

_____

6. You don't remember the number of your friend who lives nearby. How do you get the number?_____

7. You need help from the operator for a call outside the area code. What do you dial? _____

8. If you call and the line is busy, where do you get your money back after you hang up?_____

97

B. White Pages

GRANDON WHITE PAGES
For helpful community information
see Special Features Section at the back of this directory

A

ABC Hardware Store	986-7234
Abbott Chas T 121 Triangle Pl	985-5648
Abbott Leonard L 33 Maple St	986-9988
Abbott Paul	986-2321
Adams Funeral Homes Inc 12 Main St	986-4448
Allen Michael J 33 Oak Dr	986-7676
Allen Michael J 45 Blast Ave	985-0001
Alvord A R S 1702 State Blvd	985-3289
AMBULANCE SERVICE	See "Yellow Pages"
In an emergency	Dial 911
Armenian Cultural Center 67 Post St	986-7770

---

1. What do you find in the white pages of the telephone book? _____
_____

2. What are the exchange numbers (first three digits) for this City of Grandon? _____

3. You want to call a Mr. Abbott in Grandon. What more information do you need to find the number? _____
What about Michael J. Allen? _____

4. Where would you find the number for ambulance service? _____
_____

What should you do in an emergency? _____

5. What will you find in the special features section of this directory?
_____

6. An Armenian just moved into this town and feels very alone and homesick. What would you recommend? _____
_____

7. Why are new phone books printed every year? _____
_____

8. You need a taxi quickly, but you aren't familiar with any taxi in Grandon. Should you look in the white pages or somewhere else?
_____

9. You need to buy a hammer but decide to call first to see if the store is open. What number do you dial? _____

98

C. Yellow Pages

The yellow pages contain the names of businesses, service agencies, and the names of lawyers and doctors, listed alphabetically under headings that name the product or service. Get a phone directory and look up the address and number of the businesses listed below. Give a reason why you chose that business. Were the size, pictures or words important?

1. Italian restaurant _____

_____

2. Dentist _____

_____

3. Automobile dealer _____

_____

4. Washing machine dealer _____

_____

Are businesses sometimes listed under another category, as with "washing machines" in the category of appliances? _____

D. Telephone Messages

"Hello, is Mr. Kane there? . . . No? I see. Well, this is Kitty Carson of Hoffmin's Plastics Company, and I'd like to leave a message because it's 1:30 and I have to be out of the office all afternoon. Please tell him that yesterday, July 15th, was our last day of the inventory check and so we're ready to bring over the supplies Mr. Kane ordered. A delivery person will be there tomorrow at 9:00 A.M. if that's OK with him. Have him call my secretary in any case. Thanks."

Write the above message on the form below.

```
┌──────────────────────────────────────────────┐
│            WHILE YOU WERE OUT                  │
│  Date: _____ Time: _____         │
│  For: _____             │
│  From: _____             │
│    Phone #: _____             │
│      ☐ Telephoned      ☐ Please call back      │
│      ☐ Will call back  ☐ Returned your call    │
│  Message: _____             │
│  _____              │
│  _____              │
│  Message taken by: _____             │
└──────────────────────────────────────────────┘
```

E. Long Distance Rates

	Direct Distance Dialed-Station to Station						Operator-Assisted	
	Weekday Mon-Fri 8 A.M.-5 P.M.		Evening Sun-Fri 5 P.M.-11 P.M.		Night & Weekend All days 11 P.M.-8 A.M. Sat 8 A.M. to 11 P.M. Sun 8 A.M. to 5 P.M.		All Days & Hours	
	Initial First Minute	Each Additional Minute	Initial First Minute	Each Additional Minute	Initial First Minute	Each Additional Minute	Initial First Minute	Each Additional Minute
Morgan	.50	.45	.32	.28	.20	.18	1.55	.46
Fairfax	.60	.55	.38	.33	.24	.20	3.55	.55
Golpher	.75	.62	.45	.42	.30	.34	4.00	.60

1. Bob called directly to his girlfriend in Morgan last Monday night at 7:00 P.M. and talked for 10 minutes. How much was the call?

   _____

2. Mr. Tamako phoned his wife in Fairfax with the help of an operator and spoke for 2 minutes last Saturday at 11 A.M. How much was the call?_____

3. What is the cheapest time and way to call? _____

   _____

4. What is the most expensive time and way to call?_____

   _____

5. Maria will call her sister directly in Golpher next Tuesday at 3:00 P.M. and probably talk for five minutes as usual. What will the call cost her? _____

   _____

6. You called your friend in Fairfax directly last Friday night at 11:30 P.M. and spoke for 15 minutes. Alice Dim made an operator assisted call to the same place at the same hour for the same length of time. What was the price difference? _____

   _____

IX. Problem Solving

Charles received his phone bill and was ready to pay it when he noticed that there was a long distance call to an unknown place for 17 dollars. He was sure that no one in the house called there. He asked his brother who had been in the United States longer if he should complain about it. His brother just laughed and said, "Forget it. It's more trouble to complain about it. Don't be cheap. Pay the bill as it is." What should Charles do?

A. What is the problem?_____
_____
_____
_____

B. What are all the possible solutions?_____
_____
_____
_____

C. What is the best solution? _____
_____
_____
_____

UNIT 5

EMERGENCIES

There can be moments of medical emergency when the ability to communicate quickly and correctly is crucial, sometimes a matter of life and death. The following unit presents situations and a vocabulary that can be helpful when it becomes urgent to cope with an accident or natural disaster.

Objectives

Competencies:
Poisoning
First Aid
Disaster Information

Structure:
Articles
Gerunds

Pronunciation:
short a (ă)
short a (ă) / short e (ĕ)
B / V and W / V

I. Vocabulary

A. Emergency

```
                    Medicine Cabinet Contents

two-inch bandage roll        gauze squares
Band-Aids                    a roll of adhesive tape
elastic bandage              aspirin or acetaminophen
thermometer                  absorbent cotton
cotton-tipped swabs          bottle of hydrogen peroxide (3%)
prescription medicines       heating pad/hot water bottle

nonprescription medicines: antacids, laxatives, antidiarrhea
    remedies, calamine lotion, antibacterial skin cleanser,
    hexachlorophene.
```

1. first aid
2. poisoning
3. swallow
4. harmful
5. safety packaging
6. overdose
7. child resistant caps
8. bleeding
9. wound
10. extensive injury
11. press firmly
12. burns and scalds:
    1st, 2nd, 3rd degree

13. shock
14. broken bones
15. eye contamination
16. rescue breathing
17. cardiopulmonary
    resuscitation (CPR)
18. safety
19. danger/dangerous
20. hazard/hazardous
21. risk/risky

B. Situations

1. Accidents:
   home
   outdoor
   bike
   car
   fire
   gun
   sport
   animal bites

2. Disasters:
   earthquake
   flood
   storm (rain, snow,
      thunder)
   hurricane

   typhoon
   tidal wave
   cyclone
   volcano eruption
   flash flood

3. catastrophe
4. collision
5. blast
6. explosion
7. crash
8. wreck
9. gas leak
10. chemical spill
11. nuclear energy/
    radiation

II. Getting Started

A.

B.

Picture A

1. Describe what's in the picture.
2. How would you prevent a possible accident like this from happening?
3. Do child poisoning accidents happen often in your native country?

Picture B

1. Describe what's in the picture.
2. What would the best way to prevent accidents that happen to children crossing the street?
3. Do traffic accidents with children happen often in your native country?

Pictures A and B

1. Describe those things that are the same and those things that are different in both pictures.
2. Hidejko's son grabbed some dangerous medicine from the medicine cabinet and locked himself in his room. When Hidejko noticed this, she knocked on the door and yelled but the boy wouldn't open up. What should she do?

III. Conversation

A.

1. Anything interesting happen to you over the weekend?
2. Yes, I went to take a quiet walk in the neighborhood on Sunday morning and I got quite a surprise.

1. What happened?
2. A police car pulled up suddenly flashing its light. Then a fire truck, another police car from the opposite direction, and finally an ambulance arrived.

1. It seemed like a big deal. Or was it a false alarm?
2. My neighbor had a heart attack.

1. I guess at that time of the morning all services were available.
2. Well, too many emergency vehicles are better than none at all.

B.

1. A lot of accidents happen around the house.
2. You never know if it's your turn next. You should always be prepared.

1. How's that?
2. Always have the emergency phone number ready and know what to do until help comes.

1. Like for bleeding, burns, electric shock, and choking?
2. Yes, and heart attacks, seizures, or poisoning, too.

1. I've seen some advice in the first part of the phone book about that.
2. You can take classes in rescue breathing and first aid at a hospital or the Red Cross.

1. Thanks a lot for the good tips.
2. Don't mention it.

C.

1. Did you hear about Mrs. Johnson's son?
2. No, what happened?

1. He swallowed one of her prescription drugs that he found in her medicine cabinet.
2. Did she find out about it right away?

1. Luckily she did. Then she rushed him to the hospital.
2. Is he OK now?

1. Yes, they pumped out his stomach and that was it.
2. She should have kept her strong medicines in a safer place, out of the reach of her children.

1. She realizes that now. She told me that she has locks on everything that has something poisonous in it.
2. That's good, but it's a risky way to learn about keeping your home hazard-free.

Dialogue Puzzle: With a partner fill in the appropriate responses or questions in the spaces below, then practice and read to the rest of the class.

1. _____
2. There was a big storm there last week and many people had to flee their homes.

1. _____
2. They went to a Red Cross shelter in a nearby city.

1. How long did they stay there?
2. _____

1. I imagine there was medical care there.
2. _____

1. _____
2. It's a free service when disasters happen.

1. _____
2. I hope nothing serious like that hits our area.

Discussion: Answer the following questions about things talked about in the previous conversations.

1. What seems to be a common household accident?
2. What are the differences between emergency vehicles here and your native country?
3. What was the worst national disaster to hit your native country?
4. Have you ever hurt yourself in your home? How did it happen? How could it have been prevented?
5. What's the best way to act during an emergency if you are not the victim?

IV. Reading

A. Vocabulary

prevent	scared	live wire	in the nick of time
household	chemicals	tripped	either/or
harmful	poison ivy	approach	hurricane
shock	potluck	set/on fire	food poisoning

B. Reading

Maria Gomez got out of her sister's car a few minutes before class began. She crossed the parking lot of the adult school and ran into one of her classmates, Chris Wong. They greeted each other and headed to class. It was a sunny day and Chris told Maria about the latest news of a hurricane that was hitting the East Coast. When they got to the classroom, they waited outside and continued talking.

"There was a terrible accident in our neighborhood yesterday," Maria said. "A lady was cleaning her bathroom and added some household bleach to a toilet bowl cleaner and the chemicals mixed together and gave off a poisonous gas."

"Really?" Chris asked. "Then what happened?"

"The ambulance came and took her to the hospital. I think she's OK but it scared her family. I've heard that people can die by inhaling those harmful fumes."

"I would think so," Chris said. "When I was a teenager back in Taiwan, my little brother was playing with matches and almost set the house on fire. Luckily, my dad found him in the nick of time. I think home accidents are the worst and most common problem. I had a bad case of poison ivy when I was young, and my older brother got an electric shock, and my mother broke her leg by tripping over my sister's toys."

"Yes, it's really a good idea to be prepared to prevent home accidents, and know what to do if one happens," Maria said.

Just then Gino Gotelli approached the classroom and said hello.

"Are you ready for the potluck party on Saturday?" he asked with a big smile.

"Of course, with the way I cook," Chris answered, "there might be another emergency. I'll either burn the house down or we'll all get food poisoning."

106

C. Exercises

1. Put these sentences in the correct time sequence of the story, using a 1 for what came first all the way to 7 as last.

    _____ a. Maria's neighbor was taken to the hospital.
    _____ b. Gino Gotelli arrived at the classroom.
    _____ c. Chris Wong's brother almost set the house on fire.
    _____ d. Maria Gomez's sister left her off at school.
    _____ e. Chris talked about his cooking.
    _____ f. Chris greeted Maria.
    _____ g. Maria's neighbor added the bleach to the toilet bowl cleaner.

2. Write *true* or *false.*

    _____ a. Maria drove to school.
    _____ b. There had been a big storm on the East Coast.
    _____ c. Maria's neighbor died from inhaling poisonous fumes.
    _____ d. Chris had an accident-free household in his youth.
    _____ e. Chris's mom broke her leg.
    _____ f. Gino was looking forward to the party.
    _____ g. Chris didn't consider himself a gourmet cook.

3. Vocabulary: Put the vocabulary words from Section A (page 106) in the blank spaces.

    a. The police arrived _____ before the thief could get away.

    b. You can get a bad _____ if you touch a _____ .

    c. She doesn't like any _____ in her food.

    d. There is absolutely nothing _____ for a baby in their _____ .

    e. I saw an ad about how to _____ forest fires.

    f. He's _____ of snakes.

    g. I read about _____ at that restaurant. It was terrible that so many people got sick.

    h. The _____ is supposed to _____ the coast by tomorrow.

    i. The child unfortunately _____ the house _____ by playing with matches.

107

j. _____ you have a _____ where everyone brings food _____ you cook all the food yourself.

k. Have you ever got _____ while hiking? It makes me itch.

l. He _____ over the wire and fell down.

V. Structure

Articles

The is a definite article for singular or plural nouns whose identity is clear and known.

    The accident I saw last night was horrible.

A and an are indefinite articles for singular nouns whose identity is of a general class.

    She's interested in a course on safety education.

An comes before a word beginning with a vowel.

    You should drive carefully to avoid an accident.

Notice the difference between the use of the definite and indefinite articles in the examples below.

    Is there a bike at that house?
    Where is the bike that I like?

    He took a roll of adhesive tape.
    The roll of adhesive tape is almost finished.

    Is there a bathroom there?
    The bathroom in our house is too small.

    A woman is waiting outside for you.
    The woman you described is here.

Exercise S-1: Write in the correct article.

1. _____ school I attend provides _____ good education.

2. Washington, DC, _____ capital of _____ United States, is _____ beautiful city to visit on _____ trip to _____ East.

3. They picked up _____ books that were on _____ floor in your room.

4. _____ interesting thing happened to me on _____ bus yesterday.

108

No article comes before the names of persons, countries, cities, streets, or towns when they are proper nouns.

> He lives in Burlingame on the corner of Third and Main Street.
> Ms. Cork is planning to visit Taiwan and Thailand.

If these words are used as adjectives, then they come after an article.

> The Mexico City earthquake was terrible.

Names of rivers, mountains, and such have the when they contain an adjective.

> the Atlantic Ocean   the Rocky Mountains   the United States

Nouns of indefinite quantity or quality (things in general) don't have an article.

> Uranium is a valuable metal.
> Love is important.
> Rice is cheaper in my native country.

When these nouns show a particular quantity or quality, they have the article the.

> The uranium in the warehouse is missing.
> He felt the love of his family.
> I like the rice they sell in that store.

No article is used when a noun is described by a person's name or possessive pronoun.

> Lionel's job   his education

Exercise S-2: Write in the correct article, if necessary.

1. Some of _____ most important products that _____ United States imports from _____ Guatemala are _____ bananas and _____ coffee.

2. He enjoys swimming in _____ Pacific Ocean on _____ warm day near _____ Santa Barbara.

3. You can take _____ bus to the shopping center that you like by looking at _____ schedule on _____ wall over there.

4. _____ price of _____ gold is rising on _____ world market.

5. _____ Los Angeles storm destroyed _____ Mr. Garcia's home.

6. _____ Los Angeles is _____ city with many tourist attractions.

7. _____ Honesty is the best policy.

8. The principal admired _____ honesty of the student.

9. A lot of _____ rain and _____ sun are necessary for _____ crops in that country.

10. I like to study _____ safety education, but _____ safety education he teaches is boring.

Exercise S-3: Write in the correct article, if <u>necessary.</u>

Yesterday I received _____ book from _____ friend. _____ title of _____ book is "My Romantic Life" by Madame X. It is _____ interesting book, full of _____ adventure and of course _____ romance. It also has many photographs of _____ many places she visited in _____ her life. I'm sure that I will spend many hours looking at _____ photographs and thinking about _____ book's story. If I wrote _____ book someday about _____ history of my romantic adventures, I wonder what _____ public would think about it.

| **Infinitives** |

An infinitive is a verb form that expresses the general sense of the verb without a subject. It is formed with <u>to</u> and the present form of the verb, and comes after or before the main verb.

I want <u>to begin.</u>

<u>To succeed</u> is his only goal.

Many times an infinitive has an object after it.

He plans <u>to study CPR.</u>

<u>To fill out the application</u> is the most important thing.

Exercise S-4: Write the infinitive form of the verbs in parentheses.

1. (take) My cousin wants _____ a CPR class.
2. (press) He tried _____ firmly on the cut.
3. (wreck) _____ the car wasn't his intention.

Write your own infinitives in the spaces.

1. She wants _____ about taking care of a person in shock.
2. The lifeguard forgot _____ .
3. _____ is a fun thing to do.
4. My friends came to the United States _____ .
5. He doesn't like _____ before dinner.

110

Gerunds

A gerund has the form of a verb but it acts like a noun, either the subject or object of the sentence. The gerund is formed with the present form of the verb plus <u>ing</u>.

> The workers finished <u>reading.</u> (Object of the sentence)
>
> <u>Jogging</u> is a popular exercise. (Subject of the sentence)

Sometimes gerunds also have their own objects after them.

> The workers finished <u>reading</u> <u>the</u> <u>pamphlet</u> about burns.

Gerunds come after all prepositions in English except the preposition <u>to</u> when it is part of the infinitive.

> They are tired <u>from</u> <u>preparing</u> for the flood.
>
> They are worried <u>about</u> <u>cleaning</u> <u>up</u> the chemical spill.

Exercise S-5: Write the gerund of the verbs in parentheses.

1. (keep) He talked about _____ calm during a disaster.
2. (be) The boss can't blame him for _____ lazy.
3. (buy) She is thinking about _____ medicine with child resistant caps.
4. (practice) _____ first aid isn't as easy as it sounds.

Exercise S-6: Write your own gerunds in the spaces.

1. I don't feel like _____ .
2. They aren't interested in _____ .
3. He has no intention of _____ .
4. _____ is my favorite outdoor activity.
5. _____ seems like a risky thing to do.

Certain verbs come before either gerunds or infinitives. Some of these verbs are: <u>start, begin, continue, like, neglect, hate, cease, love, prefer,</u> and <u>intend.</u>

> He began <u>listening</u> to others.
> He began <u>to listen</u> to others.
>
> He will continue <u>studying</u> English.
> He will continue <u>to study</u> English.

Exercise S-7: Complete sentence A with a gerund and B with an infinitive.

1. (talk)

A. Mrs. Cook hates _____ about disasters.

B. _____

2. (bleed)

A My cousin started _____ after she cut herself.

B. _____

3. (help)

A. They like _____ others.

B. _____

4. (use)

A. They will begin _____ safety packaging.

B. _____

5. (go)

A. She loves _____ shopping.

B. _____

6. (inform)

A. The business neglected _____ the authorities of the gas leak.

B. _____

Exercise S-8: Write your own sentences with a gerund after the main verb in A and an infinitive in B. The main verb is in parenthesis.

Example: (like)

I like waking up early.

I like to wake up early.

1. (hate)

A. _____

B. _____

2. (prefer)

A. _____

B. _____

3. (begin)

A. _____

B. _____

4. (continue)

A. _____

B. _____

Exercise S-9: Answer these questions using a gerund.

1. What did the paramedic stop doing?

   _____

2. What did the policeman talk about?

   _____

3. What did the fireman enjoy doing?

   _____

Remember that gerunds are different from the continuous verb tenses.

<u>Swimming</u> is fun. (Gerund)
He<u>'s</u> <u>swimming</u> in the pool. (Present Continuous)

I enjoy <u>learning</u> new things. (Gerund)
I <u>will</u> <u>be</u> <u>learning</u> CPR next week. (Future Continuous)

They<u>'re</u> <u>considering</u> <u>investigating</u> the victim of the drug overdose. (Present Continuous/Gerund)

We use gerunds after the expressions <u>to</u> <u>be</u> <u>worth</u> and <u>no</u> <u>use</u>.

That job <u>is</u> <u>worth</u> <u>applying</u> for. It pays quite well.

It<u>'s</u> <u>no</u> <u>use</u> <u>filling</u> out that form. They only accept the new ones now.

Gerunds come after certain verbs like the following: <u>enjoy, mind, stop, consider, appreciate,</u> and <u>finish.</u>

They didn't mind helping you.

She stopped smoking.

We finished putting on the bandage.

I appreciated learning first aid.

Exercise S-10: Write your own examples of the following main verbs followed by a gerund.

1. (enjoy) _____

2. (mind) _____

3. (no use)_____

4. (consider) _____

5. (to be worth) _____

6. (appreciate) _____

7. (stop) _____

8. (finish) _____

VI. Composition

Exercise C-1: Write words of your choice according to the descriptions below each space. After you finish, let your teacher correct and then read aloud.

I think that the worst kind of home accident is _____
                                                       (name of accident)

because _____ .
                        (sentence)

One way to be prepared is by _____ . A home
                         (gerund + object)

accident that I heard about once was when _____
                                            (sentence)

_____ .

There are different kinds of natural disasters like earthquakes, floods, hurricanes, typhoons, storms, and drought. The worst disaster that ever happened in my native country was _____
                                        (disaster)

on _____ in _____ . Many
       (date)   (city or region)

people _____ and there was _____
        (what happened)   (a lot/a little)

physical damage. The rescue operations were _____ .
                                        (adjective)

Sometimes other kinds of disasters happen like plane, train or bus crashes, boats sinking, fires, and explosions. A very bad accident of this kind was _____ in _____
                (accident)   (country)

in _____ . It was terrible because _____
      (year)

_____ .
                          (sentence)

Sometimes people are heroic when accidents occur because _____

_____ .
                          (sentence)

VII. Pronunciation

A. Vowel:

short a or (ă)

1. accident	2. hazzard	3. package
dance	antacid	gas
pad	aspirin	disaster

4. That passenger was in the last crash.

5. The blast in the factory came from a tank.

Contrast: short a (ă) / short e (ĕ)

6. bad/bed	7. gas/guess	8. than/then
fad/fed	bag/beg	past/pest
jam/gem	dance/dense	mat/met

B. Consonants:

B / V and V / W

1. ban/van
   berry/very
   boat/vote
   robe/rove

2. vine/wine
   veal/we'll
   vest/west
   grove/grow

3. The very best marble made the place look bigger.

4. Walt went west to solve the wine problem.

VIII. Life Skills

A. Poisoning

There are over 250,000 different non-food household items that can become poisonous when used incorrectly. Is your home poison-proof? Check this list for possible dangers in your home.

YES	NO	
		Bathroom
☐	☐	1. Do aspirin and other potentially harmful products have child-resistant caps?
☐	☐	2. Have you removed all out-of-date prescription medicines?
		Kitchen
☐	☐	3. Do all harmful products in the cabinets like furniture polishes, drain cleaners and some oven cleaners have safety packaging?
☐	☐	4. Are all potentially harmful products in their original containers?
☐	☐	5. Are these products stored away from food?
☐	☐	6. Are these products out of reach of children? Locking all cabinets that have dangerous products is good poison prevention.
☐	☐	7. Have medicines been removed from kitchen counters and medicines, especially when near look-alike vitamin pill bottles?
		Garage or Storage Area
☐	☐	8. Do poisons such as charcoal lighter fluid, paint thinner, antifreeze and turpentine have their original labels and are in their original containers?
☐	☐	9. Do these products have child resistant caps?
☐	☐	10. Are these products out of reach of children?
☐	☐	11. Are any potentially harmful products stored in drinking glasses or bottles?
		House
☐	☐	12. Do you know if any plants that you have in your home are poisonous?
☐	☐	13. Do you have an emergency number for poisoning handy by your telephone?

115

B. First Aid in the Home

Burns and Scalds

1. All burns and scalds: immerse burned area immediately in cold water or apply clean, moist towels until pain stops. Following water treatment, cover burns with a clean cloth to exclude air. Do not break blisters. See a doctor as soon as possible.

2. For severe burns: call your hospital or doctor immediately. Immerse burned areas as above until help arrives. Prevent shock by covering victim and having him lie down with legs elevated.

3. For chemical burns: call your hospital or doctor immediately. Flush skin with lots of running water until help arrives.

---

1. Bob is in the kitchen cooking dinner when he accidentally burns himself on the stove. What should he do?

   _____

   _____

2. Margaret got a minor burn and treated it with water and moist towels. She notices a blister forming and thinks it's so ugly that she'd better break it. You come into the room. What would you tell her?

   _____

   _____

3. Your friend got severe burns from a fire in the kitchen. She goes into shock, her face turning pale with chills and nausea, and her skin is cold and clammy, her breathing shallow. What should she do?

   _____

   _____

4. A laboratory technician working with acid spills some on his face. You are working beside him. What should you do?

   _____

   _____

C. Disaster Information

The American National Red Cross Information for Disaster Victims

If you need help, go to the nearest Red Cross disaster service center. When disaster strikes, Red Cross can help you immediately with:

— Food, clothing and rent
— Urgent household needs
— Medical, nursing and hospital care
— Temporary repairs to your home so that you can move back in
— Replacement of personal occupational supplies and equipment
— The Red Cross will provide information regarding government and other private agencies that may be of further help to you. If no such resources are available, Red Cross may give you additional assistance for your recovery.

Red Cross deals personally with each family's situation. Your Red Cross is the agency through which the American people voluntarily help you to recover from the disaster. All Red Cross help is free, a gift from the American people. Red Cross disaster services are financed solely by voluntary contributions.

Please bring identification that shows where you lived at the time of the disaster. This will help us to help you.

1. There's a flood in Northern California after many days of hard rain. All the residents of a small town must evacuate their homes. Where will they live until their homes are dry again?

   _____

   _____

2. After a terrible tornado in the Midwest, one family loses its home and goes to the Red Cross disaster service center. What services are available for them?

   _____

   _____

3. A hurricane hits the Southeast. What should a family bring to the disaster center?

   _____

   _____

4. What sort of disaster can happen in your part of the country? Do you know what to do if a disaster strikes? What sort of things should you keep in your home in case of an emergency? Is there a Red Cross agency near you? Is there another kind of disaster emergency service agency in the area?

   _____

   _____

117

IX. Problem Solving

Mr. Tan keeps a loaded gun in one of his drawers in his bedroom because he thinks it's good protection against possible thieves. His wife feels a little nervous with it because their two daughters are getting older, now age three and five, and she read an article in the paper about a child's shooting herself. Mr. Tan thinks his wife worries too much. "We have to be ready to protect ourselves," he says. "And, anyway, girls are never curious about guns." Mrs. Tan still feels uneasy. What should Mrs. Tan do?

A. What is the problem?_____

_____

_____

_____

B. What are all the possible solutions?_____

_____

_____

_____

C. What solution do you think is best?_____

_____

_____

_____

UNIT 6

JOBS

Finding a job or getting a better one, reading classified ads in the newspaper, presenting oneself well in a job interview, understanding job responsibilities and working conditions, applying for a Social Security card are all things that can be extremely difficult for someone new to this country. This unit will deal with this important part of survival—work.

Objectives

Competencies:
   Classified Ads
   Qualifications
   Work Duties
   Working Conditions
   Interview
   Social Security Application

Structure:
   Adverbs (Differences between Adjectives and Adverbs)
      Comparative and Superlative
   Present Perfect and Present Perfect Continuous

Pronunciation:
   long i (ī)
   long i (ī) / short i (ĭ)
   L / R and S / Z

I. Vocabulary

A. Job Vocabulary

1. employment/job/work
2. occupation/profession/career
3. to work/employ/hire
4. employer/boss
5. employee/worker
6. position
7. to be self-employed
8. wages/salary
9. contract
10. paycheck/payday
11. workday
12. day off
13. overtime
14. job offer/job opening
15. fire/dismiss/lose a job
16. to lay off/layoff
17. earn money
18. make money
19. minimum wage
20. interview
21. application/apply/applicant
22. qualify/qualification
23. employment agency
24. classified ad/want ad
25. résumé
26. letter of recommendation
27. retire/retirement
28. pension
29. Social Security (number)
30. shift
    day:
    8:00/9:00 A.M.—4:00/5:00 P.M.
    swing/evening:
    4:00/5:00 P.M.—12:00 A.M.
    night/graveyard:
    12:00 A.M.—8:00 A.M.
31. benefits:
    medical insurance
    dental coverage
    paid vacations
    holidays
    workman's compensation

B. Kinds of Jobs

1. Mechanical/Repair
   auto mechanic, locksmith, TV and radio service technician, plumber
2. Driving/Operating
   bus driver, machine tool operator, pilot
3. Clerical
   bank teller, secretary, cashier, postal clerk
4. Physical
   carpenter, farm laborer, electrician, miner
5. Care/Help
   dental assistant, counselor, teacher, nurse
6. Creative/Artistic
   dancer, model, commercial artist, editor
7. Sales
   auto salesperson, gas station attendant, retail salesworker
8. Service
   cosmetologist, fry cook, waiter/waitress, security guard
9. Science
   chemist, physicist, geologist

II. Getting Started

A.

B.

Picture A

1. Describe what's in the picture.
2. What skills does the worker in the picture need for that job?
3. What is this job like in your native country?

Picture B

1. Describe what's in the picture.
2. What skills does the worker in this picture need for that job?
3. What is this job like in your native country?

Pictures A and B

1. Describe those things that are the same in both pictures and those things that are different.
2. Ed has a wife and two kids and is paying for a home. He is really bored at work. It's the same thing every day, no changes, but the pay is very good. What should he do?

III. Conversation

A.

1. I got a new job yesterday.
2. What are you doing?

1. I'm a supervisor at a local hotel.
2. Is it a good job?

1. Yes, it's really good. I'm in charge of several workers. I have to make sure that they do their work properly and on time.
2. That's a lot of responsibility. I had a job like that once and I enjoyed it quite a bit. Of course, everything depends on the management.

1. I like the way they run this hotel. Everyone is so courteous and thoughtful.
2. That's very important. If there's a good atmosphere to work in, then a job can be a pleasure.

1. I agree with you on that. It's one of the reasons why I left my old job.
2. Well, I wish you the best of luck. Let me know when you get a promotion or a raise.

B.

1. I used to have a very nice office job in my native country.
2. That's a familiar problem with many refugees that I have talked to. What are you doing now?

1. I do manual work in a factory.
2. Is it a part-time or full-time job?

1. Unfortunately, it's full time. I'm really tired when I get home.
2. Do you have a university education from your native country?

1. Yes, but it isn't worth much here. I would have to go back to school if I wanted the same type of job that I had in my native country.
2. You should go and see a job counselor at the Employment Development Department. He can probably give you some advice.

C.

1. Good morning. I heard that you have a job opening for a clerk.
2. Yes, we do. It starts on the 15th. Would you like to fill out an application?

1. Yes, please. What are the hours like?
2. Monday through Friday, 8:00 to 4:30. Here is a job description that will tell you about the duties, the salary, and the qualifications.

1. Thank you very much. Is there a deadline?
2. Yes, this coming Friday is the last day that they will accept applications.

1. I'd better fill this out right here and now. When will they notify the applicants?
2. They'll interview the final two or three candidates on next Wednesday and make their choice on the following day.

1. Thank you very much.
2. You're welcome. And good luck!

Dialogue Puzzle: With a partner fill in the appropriate responses or questions in the spaces below, then practice and read to the rest of the class.

1. _____
2. Yes, we have an opening for a secretary here.

1. _____
2. $6.75 per hour.

1. What is the work schedule?
2. _____

1. What are the qualifications?
2. _____

1. _____
2. Just fill out this application and hand it in to this desk before Friday.

1. _____
2. We will notify you by the 11th.

Discussion: Answer the following questions about things talked about in the previous conversations.

1. What kinds of jobs have you or a close relative had?
2. What is rewarding work?
3. Why do some jobs require letters of recommendation?
4. When is part-time work good?
5. What kinds of jobs have difficult qualifications?

IV. Reading

A. Vocabulary

benefits	start out	dropped
shift	made fun of	exhausted
at least	filled out	bulletin board
write down	career	in the meantime
schedule	minimum	right there on the spot
hire		

B. Reading

Juan Robles was studying for a career as an accountant in his native country in Central America, but he had to leave suddenly because of the problems of the civil war there. He came to the United States and stayed with an old friend of his family. After a short while he began to look for a job, first in the classified ads in the newspaper and then on bulletin boards at various stores around the city. He didn't find anything. His friend recommended that he at least study English in the meantime at the community adult school.

On his first day in class he talked with a man from Lebanon who told him about a job as a busboy in his brother's restaurant. Juan was interested and wrote down the address. After the class he went there and talked to the owner. The man asked Juan about his previous work experience and then hired him right there on the spot. It was minimum wage work, Tuesday through Saturday in the evening shift, with no benefits. Juan filled out an application and thanked the owner.

Juan didn't start out very well with his new employment. He dropped and broke a dish in the middle of the restaurant, spilled water on one customer, and took the dish away too early from another who got up to go to the restroom. The worst thing was when one customer took out a cigarette and asked for a light. Juan went to the kitchen and brought back a flashlight. Several people made fun of him. One of the waiters then came with a box of matches.

Juan returned home exhausted. He went to sleep and dreamed of being so rich that he never had to work again.

123

C. Exercises

1. Write these sentences in the correct time sequence of the story, using a 1 for what happened first, all the way to 7 as last.

   _____ a. Juan filled out the job application.

   _____ b. The waiter gave the customer matches.

   _____ c. Juan was studying to be an accountant.

   _____ d. Juan picked up a flashlight.

   _____ e. The Lebanese man talked about a job opening.

   _____ f. Juan went to the adult school.

   _____ g. The restaurant owner hired a new busboy.

2. Write *true* or *false*.

   _____ a. Juan left his country under difficult circumstances.

   _____ b. Juan stayed with a relative.

   _____ c. Jobs are listed in the classified section of the newspaper.

   _____ d. Juan found a job by talking with a classmate.

   _____ e. Juan worked as a busboy during lunchtime.

   _____ f. Some of the customers laughed at Juan.

   _____ g. Juan misunderstood the word "light."

3. Vocabulary: Put the vocabulary words from Section A (page 123) in the blank spaces.

   a. He will _____ your hours on the new work _____ .

   b. The kids _____ the boy with the hole in his pants.

   c. She copied the phone number from the _____ .

   d. I _____ the application _____ .

   e. _____ he sent you a birthday card.

   f. Mr. Johnson was so _____ that he just _____ on the sofa.

   g. She wanted a _____ in medicine. _____ she studied hard and saved her money.

   h. The workers always _____ slowly on the graveyard _____ .

   i. They will _____ you but the job doesn't offer any _____ .

   j. The boss wants a _____ of twelve new orders by Monday.

V. Structure

An adverb is a word that describes 1) a verb, 2) an adjective or 3) another adverb.

1) adverb/verb   She talks <u>quickly.</u>
2) adverb/adjective   He is a <u>very</u> clever mechanic.
3) adverb/adverb   The driver was <u>only</u> slightly hurt.

A. Four kinds of adverbs describe verbs:

1. <u>Adverb of Time:</u> It answers the question, "When?"
   Examples: early, soon, today, now, recently
   The manager will tell you about overtime <u>later.</u>
   (<u>Later</u> is the adverb that answers the question, "When will the manager tell you about overtime?")

2. <u>Adverb of Place:</u> It answers the question, "Where?"
   Examples: here, near, far, close
   She's going <u>there.</u>
   (<u>There</u> is the adverb that answers the question, "Where is she going?")

3. <u>Adverb of Manner:</u> It answers the question, "How?"
   Examples: badly, slowly, well
   The receptionist spoke <u>loudly.</u>
   (<u>Loudly</u> is the adverb that answers the question, "How does the receptionist speak?")

4. <u>Adverb of Frequency:</u> It answers the question, "How often?"
   Examples: never, seldom, rarely, sometimes, often, always
   He <u>always</u> wants to do good work.
   (<u>Always</u> is the adverb that answers the question, "How often does he want to do good work?")

B. One kind of adverb describes adjectives:

1. <u>Adverb of Measure or Degree:</u> It answers the question, "How much or how little?"
   Examples: too, so, extremely
   The applicant looks <u>very</u> nervous.
   (<u>Very</u> is the adverb that answers the question, "How nervous does the applicant look?")

C. One kind of adverb describes other adverbs:

1. <u>Adverb</u> <u>of</u> <u>Measure:</u> It answers the question, "How much or how little?"

   Examples: too, only, very

       He became upset <u>quite</u> suddenly.

   (<u>Quite</u> is the adverb that answers the question, "How suddenly did he become upset?")

Exercise S-1: Underline the adverbs.

1. The workers will go on strike tomorrow.
2. The job was too good to be true.
3. The students felt completely exhausted after the exam.
4. His suit looked only slightly wrinkled during the interview.
5. She carefully wrote her résumé.
6. The employment agency will open soon.
7. You seldom look for jobs in the classified ads.

You can form many adverbs by adding -ly to the adjective.

    slow—slowly

If an adjective ends in -l, add -ly; if it ends in -e, take away the -e and add -ly; if it ends in -y, take away the -y and add -ily; and, usually, if it ends in -ic, add -ally.

careful—carefully	happy—happily
simple—simply	specific—specifically

The adverb of the adjective <u>good</u> is <u>well</u>.

    He speaks English well.

These adjectives are the same as adverbs: <u>high, fast, hard, late, low, straight, deep, near.</u>

    Adjective: It is a <u>high</u> building.

    Adverb: The airplane flew <u>high</u>.

    Adjective: The <u>fast</u> car screeched to a halt.

    Adverb: She drove <u>fast</u>.

Notice that some of these adverbs exist but have a different meaning from the words above.

highly = greatly	They are highly recommended.
hardly = scarcely, barely	She could hardly walk.
deeply = strong emotion	She cares deeply for him.

A few adjectives like <u>friendly</u> and <u>lovely</u> end in -ly. Remember that they describe the noun or pronoun, not the verb.

    They are <u>friendly</u> people.   It's a <u>lovely</u> day.

Exercise S-2: Change these adjectives to adverbs. Then try to form a sentence using each adverb.

1. rapid _____

_____

2. easy _____

_____

3. hopeful _____

_____

4. true _____

_____

5. clear _____

_____

6. automatic _____

_____

7. terrible _____

_____

8. day _____

_____

9. suitable _____

_____

10. scientific _____

_____

Exercise S-3: Write two sentences, one with an adjective, the other with its corresponding adverb. Choose from the list in the above exercise and underline them.

Example: He is <u>nice.</u>
He sings <u>nicely.</u>

1. (adjective) _____
   (adverb) _____
2. (adjective) _____
   (adverb) _____
3. (adjective) _____
   (adverb) _____

Exercise S-4: Adjectives or adverbs? Underline the correct one in each sentence.

1. The secretary is a (slow/slowly) typist.
2. The new students speak English quite (good/well).

3. She dressed (careless/carelessly).
4. It was a very (impressive/impressively) résumé.
5. Benefits are (good/well) for employees.
6. The workers listened (attentive/attentively) to their boss.
7. The policeman gave us the (correct/correctly) directions.
8. I felt (angry/angrily).
9. The truck driver drove off (quick/quickly).
10. The food is (delicious/deliciously).

Exercise S-5: Choose an adverb to complete the sentences.

1. She doesn't _____ attend class.
2. Your friend is _____ tired.
3. She _____ walked to her office.
4. They speak French rather _____ .
5. He drove _____ after work.
6. You should _____ take care of your health.

The comparative and superlative of adverbs uses <u>more</u> and <u>most</u>.

| quickly | more quickly | most quickly |
| careful | more carefully | most carefully |

Exercise S-6: Write the correct form of the comparative and superlative of the adverbs in parentheses.

1. (respectfully) He spoke _____ than his brother.
2. (carefully) His new accountant examined the important documents _____ than the previous person.
3. (neatly) Al writes the _____ of all the students.
4. (slowly) My nephew speaks _____ than you.
5. (quietly) The child plays the _____ of all the children here.

Adverbs that are written the same as adjectives have comparatives and superlatives like adjectives.

The swing shift worked <u>harder</u> than the night shift.

They swam the <u>straightest</u> of all the swimmers.

<u>Still/Anymore</u>

<u>Still</u> as an adjective and noun means "silent or silence" and "without movement."

The forest is very <u>still.</u>

It can also have this meaning when it's an adverb.

He stood <u>still</u>.

<u>Still</u> has another meaning, "now as before," a continuing action that usually comes before the main verb.

He is <u>still</u> working in the office.

They <u>still</u> study English.

<u>Anymore</u> is used for an action that took place in the past but now it doesn't. It usually comes at the end of a negative sentence.

He isn't working there <u>anymore</u>.

They don't use typewriters <u>anymore</u>.

Exercise S-7: Write either <u>still</u> or <u>anymore</u>.

1. She is _____ working as a cashier.

2. He doesn't travel there _____ .

3. I seldom see Mohammed _____ .

4. They are _____ negotiating the salary.

5. The two nations _____ want to establish peace.

Exercise: Now make up your own sentences using <u>still</u> and <u>anymore</u>.

_____

_____

_____

<u>Too/So/Also</u>

You can combine two sentences with the same verb by using <u>too, also,</u> or <u>so</u> plus the correct helping verb. Note the word order changes for <u>so</u>.

He takes the bus. She takes the bus.

He takes the bus and she <u>does too.</u>

He takes the bus and she <u>does also.</u>

He takes the bus and <u>so does</u> she.

(Notice that the helping verb is "does" because the main verb is the present "takes." Also, it is not necessary to repeat the word "bus" after the verb.)

We visited Los Angeles. Your friends visited Los Angeles.

We visited Los Angeles and your friends <u>did too.</u>

We visited Los Angeles and your friends <u>did also.</u>

We visited Los Angeles and <u>so did</u> your friends.

(Notice that the helping verb is "did" because the main verb is the past "visited.")

Exercise S-8: Combine these sentences using <u>too,</u> <u>also,</u> or <u>so.</u>

1. The manager arrived late. The teller arrived late.

   The manager arrived late and _____ too.

   _____ also.

   _____ and so _____ .

2. My brother can speak English. My niece can speak English.

   _____ too.

   _____ also.

   _____ and so _____ .

3. Bob is in a job training program. Mary is in a job training program.

   _____ .

   _____ .

   _____ .

4. Mr. Mack got his paycheck on Friday. Mrs. Johnson got her paycheck on Friday.

   _____ .

   _____ .

   _____ .

All three forms here mean the same but <u>too</u> is used more often in conversation.

<u>Either/Neither</u>

You can combine two negative sentences with the same verb by using <u>either</u> or <u>neither.</u> Again, note the word order and the use of the helping verb that is the same tense as the main verb.

He doesn't know the minimum wage. She doesn't know the minimum wage.

He doesn't know the minimum wage and she <u>doesn't</u> <u>either.</u>

He doesn't know the minimum wage and <u>neither</u> <u>does</u> she.

Exercise S-9: Combine these negative sentences with <u>either</u> and <u>neither.</u>

1. She shouldn't work there. Her friend shouldn't work there.

   She shouldn't work there and _____ either.

   _____ and neither _____ .

2. Bob wouldn't say that. Mary wouldn't say that.

   _____ .

   _____ .

3. I didn't apply for that job. My neighbor didn't apply for that job.

   _____ .

   _____ .

Present Perfect and Present Perfect Continuous

A. Present Perfect

I have chosen	I have not chosen	Have I chosen?
You have chosen	You have not chosen	Have you chosen?
We have chosen	We have not chosen	Have we chosen?
They have chosen	They have not chosen	Have they chosen?
He has chosen	He has not chosen	Has he chosen?
She has chosen	She has not chosen	Has she chosen?
It has chosen	It has not chosen	Has it chosen?

(Contractions: have = 've / has = 's / have not = haven't / has not = hasn't)

The present perfect tense has the helping verb <u>have</u> or <u>has</u> plus the past participle of the verb.

<u>Subject</u>   +   <u>have/has</u>   +   <u>past</u> <u>participle</u> <u>of</u> <u>verb</u>

<u>The</u> <u>artist</u>   <u>has</u>   <u>finished</u> the picture.

Short answers:

    Have they seen him?

        Yes, they have. or No, they haven't.

    Has she gone yet?

        Yes, she has. or No, she hasn't.

Exercise S-10: Write the correct form of the present perfect of the verbs in parentheses.

1. (fill) _____ you ever _____ out a job application?

2. (leave) The editor _____ the room many times.

3. (return) The veterinarian _____ just _____ with the dog.

4. (not-work) Mr. Hart _____ as a supervisor before.

5. (care for/help) Since he was a young adult he _____ and _____ many people.

6. (study) Those students _____ at school since June.

7. (forget) _____ she already _____ the answer? Yes, _____ . (Short answer)

8. (not-understand) They _____ the qualifications for the job yet.

There are three uses of the present perfect:

1. To describe an action that happened at an indefinite or unknown time of the past.

    I have read that magazine.

131

(It doesn't tell you when, only at some unknown time in the past.)

He has signed a contract <u>before</u>.

I've <u>already</u> written him a letter.

Have you <u>ever</u> worked for this company?

(The underlined words are often used with this kind of present perfect.)

Exercise S-11: Write your own examples using the present perfect and these key words.

1. _____ before.

2. _____ already _____ .

3. _____ ever _____ ?

2. To describe an action that happened many times or repeatedly in the past.

I have called the baker <u>again</u> <u>and</u> <u>again</u>.

They have eaten there <u>on</u> <u>several</u> <u>occasions</u>.

My neighbor has applied for that job <u>many</u> <u>times</u>.

Exercise S-12: Write your own examples using the present perfect and these key words.

1. _____ many times.

2. _____ over and over.

3. To describe an action that began in the past and has continued up to the present, or a past action that is close to the present in time.

He has worked there <u>for</u> two years.

   (He worked there in the past and still works there now.)

We have lived here <u>since</u> June.

   (We started living here in June and we still live here now.)

Has your sister gotten a raise at her job <u>yet</u>?

   (Has she gotten a raise at any time since she started working there?)

The class has <u>just</u> begun.

   (It started a short time ago.)

Note: <u>Since</u> is used with a <u>point</u> in time, like a year, month, or date. <u>For</u> is used with a <u>quantity</u> of time, like a number of days, years, or minutes.

since 1981	for ten years
since yesterday	for a while
since January	for a few minutes
since Feb. 12, 1985	for a long time
since I was young	for two hours

Exercise S-13: Write your own examples using the present perfect and these key words.

1. _____ for _____ .
2. _____ since _____ .
3. _____ yet?
4. _____ just _____ .

The present perfect is used very often to open a conversation, especially if you don't know very much about the other person.

Have you ever been to my native country?

Have you ever tasted this kind of food?

Have you seen Mr. Dresden lately?

Practice this now with the person next to you. Have a short conversation and open it with the present perfect.

Be careful of the difference between the past verb and the present perfect.

She <u>studied</u> at that school.
(Past: She doesn't study there now.)

She <u>has studied</u> at that school since April.
(Present perfect: She studied there in the past and still studies there now.)

Exercise S-14: Write the correct verb, past or present perfect.

1. (live) They _____ in Canada from 1961 to 1975.

2. (live) I am now living on 3rd Avenue where I _____ for six years.

3. (work) Bob _____ as a cook before he started college.

4. (work) Since graduating, however, he _____ as an engineer.

5. (study) Your brother _____ all night. It's too bad he failed the test.

6. (study) Your brother _____ hard all night. He's still in his room getting ready for the test.

7. (finish) The union _____ just _____ negotiations.

8. (finish) The union _____ negotiations late last night.

9. (leave/live) Mr. Wong _____ St. Louis a few days ago and _____ in Dallas since then.

10. (speak) Raffi speaks English well because he _____ it all his life.

B. Present Perfect Continuous

I have been speaking	I haven't been speaking	Have I been speaking?
You have been speaking	You haven't been speaking	Have you been speaking?
We have been speaking	We haven't been speaking	Have we been speaking?
They have been speaking	They haven't been speaking	Have they been speaking?
He has been speaking	He hasn't been speaking	Has he been speaking?
She has been speaking	She hasn't been speaking	Has she been speaking?
It has been speaking	It hasn't been speaking	Has it been speaking?

The present perfect continuous is used the same as the present perfect except that it stresses the continuous nature or longer time of the action.

They <u>have</u> <u>lived</u> here for five years.

They <u>have</u> <u>been</u> <u>living</u> here for five years.

(Short answers are the same present continuous.)

Exercise S-15: Write the correct form of the present perfect continuous of the verbs in parentheses.

1. (wait) The cosmetologist _____ there for fifteen minutes.

2. (talk) The sales representative _____ for more than two hours on the phone.

3. (argue) _____ they _____ about salaries all during dinner?

4. (not-study) She _____ for very long.

5. (rain) _____ it _____ all day long?
   No, _____ . (Short answer)

6. (expect) We _____ the promotions for quite a while.

7. (plan) _____ he _____ to quit his job this past year? Yes, _____ . (Short answer)

8. (not-take) She _____ it easy since she last saw you.

Exercise S-16: Answer these questions in the present perfect continuous.

1. What have you been doing for the past hour?

   _____

2. What has he been thinking about since he got fired from his job?

   _____

3. What have you been planning to do?

   _____

4. What have you been doing since I last saw you?

   _____

VI. Composition

Exercise C-1: Write words of your choice according to the descriptions below each space. After you finish, let your teacher correct and then read aloud.

Some popular jobs in the United States are _____,
(job)
_____ , and _____ . The most difficult
(job)   (job)
kind of work is _____ because _____
(job)   (sentence)
_____ . The easiest

kind of work is _____ because _____
(job)   (sentence)
_____ . The salaries of workers

here are _____ . Unions here are _____ .
(adjective)   (adjective)
There seem to be _____ opportunities for employment
(many/few)
around here. To get a good job you have to _____ .
(what to do)
In my native country the most popular kinds of jobs seem to be

_____ , _____ , and _____ .
(jobs)
The most difficult job is _____ while the easiest is
(job)
_____ . The wages for workers there are _____ .
(job)   (adjective)
Unions _____ workers for many years. The best-paying
(present perfect verb)
job you could have there would be _____ , while the lowest
(job)
would be _____ . People _____ get to work
(job)   (adverb—how often)
by _____ . To get a good job in my native country, _____
(kind of transportation)
_____ .
(sentence)
A job of the future will be _____ . I think automation
(job)
is _____ because _____
(adjective)   (sentence)
_____ .

VII. Pronunciation

A. Vowel:

long i (ī)

1. frycook	2. guide	3. qualify
fire	apply	overtime
driver	scientist	retirement

4. The miner is writing the story of his life in the library.

5. The mountain climber might try your advice.

Contrast: long i (ī) / short i (ĭ)

6. bite/bit	7. file/fill	8. kite/kit
spine/spin	rhyme/rim	ride/rid
stripe/strip	dime/dim	fine/fin

135

B. Consonants:

L / R and S / Z

1. lake/rake
   long/wrong
   collect/correct
   fly/fry

2. sink/zink
   Sue/zoo
   prices/prizes
   loose/lose

3. The crowd raced to the fire in the long store.

4. Sara sewed several zippers on those dresses.

VIII. Life Skills

A. Classified Ads

221—HELP WANTED	221—HELP WANTED
ACCOUNTANT Small CPA firm, non-smoker, salary commensurate with ability and experience. Send resume to AD #453 of this paper.	**HAIRCUTTERS** Fastcuts now hiring, full benefits, adv. training, full time; state cosmetologist's licence necessary. 785-9992.
APT. MANAGER Cpl. 16 units. Lt. duties. Rent reduction. Mark, 10-2, 474-8963.	**NURSING ASSISTANTS** With exp. All shifts. Apply: Hills Extended Care Hospital, 50 San Rafael Dr., Milltown, Mon-Fri, 8-4, 344-5566.
DENTAL RECEPT F/T, mature cheerful for respons position; exp pref, will train, 453-7564.	**SALES** P/T positions open, all shifts avail. Apply in person at Personnel Office, Baker's Dept. Store. Equal Opportunity Employer.
DISHWASHER Apply in person after 2 pm. Le Bistro Rouge, 765 3rd Ave. Big City.	**TEACHER** Credentialed and exp'd for preschool. Gd salary and benefits. Send resume to Ad #341 of this paper.
GRILL COOK Experience preferred; breakfast and lunch. Call 487-4623, ask for Eric.	

1. Write the name of the job under the category for which you would apply.

Telephone Call	Letter	In Person
_____	_____	_____
_____	_____	_____
_____	_____	_____
_____	_____	_____

2. Which jobs don't require or prefer any previous work experience?

_____

136

3. Which jobs require licenses? _____

4. Which employers say that they are Equal Opportunity Employers?

_____

What does this mean? _____

5. If John applies for the job as grill cook, will he still have time to go to school in the evenings?_____

6. Alberto and Maria are interested in the apartment manager job. How will they be paid? _____

What kind of work will they be doing? _____

7. Which jobs require résumés?_____

8. Which jobs offer benefits? _____

9. Which jobs offer training?_____

10. Mary is 18 years old and looking for her first job. Do you think she can get the job as a dental receptionist? _____

B. Qualifications

Match the job on the left with its qualifications on the right.

a. forestry aide
b. typist
c. postal clerk
d. truck driver
e. cashier
f. commercial artist
g. fry cook
h. TV and radio
   service technician

_____ 1. High school graduation preferred with courses in math, bookkeeping and typing. Need nimble fingers to work register keys quickly. Should be able to get along with people.

_____ 2. Must be at least 18 yrs. old and able to pass a four-part written test. A good memory and the ability to read rapidly and accurately are important. Window clerks should enjoy contact with customers.

_____ 3. High school graduation preferred. Expected to type at least 40-50 words a minute. Good spelling, punctuation and grammar are important. Neatness, accuracy and the ability to concentrate in noisy places are very helpful.

_____ 4. High school graduation plus art school. Art talent is important, plus the ability to come up with good ideas for illustrations.

_____ 5. High school education preferred. Driving skill and a chauffer's license needed. Good vision and hearing important. Some firms do not hire people under 25 years of age.

_____ 6. High school graduation plus electronics training through trade schools or correspondence study. Some physical strength for lifting heavy items. Need to climb on roofs to install and adjust antennas.

137

_____ 7. One or two years of special training after high school or work experience required. People with more training get more responsible jobs. Must like outdoors and be physically fit.

_____ 8. Most learn on the job as helpers. Must be able to work with others and to work under pressure. Need to have a good sense of taste and smell. Must be able to stand for a long time.

C. Work Duties

Match these jobs with their duties.

a. jeweler   e. plumber
b. boiler tender   f. bank clerk
c. firefighter   g. cosmetologist
d. furniture upholsterer   h. air-conditioner mechanic

_____ 1. Put out fires, check homes and businesses for dangers and teach fire protection to the public.

_____ 2. Sort checks, add columns of numbers, make entries in records, prepare monthly statements. May use adding machine, calculator, bookkeeping machine, typewriter and computer.

_____ 3. Operate and maintain boilers, diesel engines, turbines, generators, pumps and compressors in factories and other buildings.

_____ 4. Install or repair air-conditioning and heating units.

_____ 5. Make rings, pins, necklaces and other kinds of jewelry. Repair watches and jewelry that is damaged or worn out.

_____ 6. Cover chairs, sofas and other furniture with fabric, leather, plastic or other coverings. Repair or replace springs or other worn or damaged parts.

_____ 7. Install pipe systems that carry water, steam, air or other liquids or gases. Repair clogged or leaking pipes, sinks and drains.

_____ 8. Wash and set hair of women and men. Give permanents, tint, cut or style hair.

D. Working Conditions

Check the working conditions that each job has. Then mark your preferences.

CONDITIONS	House Painter	Dentist	Mail Carrier	Architect	YOU
Works inside					
Works outside					
Physical work					
Mental work					
Works alone					
Works with others					
Busy place					
Quiet place					
Repeats same task					
Works in variety of places					
Works with people					
Works with things					
Works with ideas					
Wears a uniform					
Wears dressy clothes					
Is supervised					
Is not supervised					

E. Interview

Check *yes* or *no* for things to do before, during, and after a job interview.

YES	NO		
☐	☐	1.	Prepare a list of questions to ask the interviewer.
☐	☐	2.	Get a good rest the night before.
☐	☐	3.	Know how you'll get there.
☐	☐	4.	Be at least 2 hours early.
☐	☐	5.	Practice answering questions with a friend before the interview.
☐	☐	6.	Have personal information with you.
☐	☐	7.	Bring a friend or relative with you.
☐	☐	8.	Wear formal clothing.
☐	☐	9.	Be neat and well-groomed.
☐	☐	10.	Address the interviewer by his or her first name.
☐	☐	11.	Be positive and confident.
☐	☐	12.	Use good posture.
☐	☐	13.	Act very friendly.
☐	☐	14.	Be polite.
☐	☐	15.	Be nervous.
☐	☐	16.	Find out all you can about the job.
☐	☐	17.	Avoid direct eye contact.
☐	☐	18.	Ask for a pen if you have to write.
☐	☐	19.	Yawn and stretch if you feel tired.
☐	☐	20.	Thank the person who interviewed you.
☐	☐	21.	Ask the interviewer to repeat something that you didn't completely understand.
☐	☐	22.	Be aggressive about finding out whether you got the job or not.
☐	☐	23.	Stop trying to get other jobs if you don't get this job.

Here are some questions that an employer might ask an applicant in a job interview. After reading them, divide into pairs, one acting as the employer who asks some of these questions and the other a person who wants a particular job. Others are to rate the applicant's answers: 1) organized/unorganized; 2) brief/lengthy; 3) concise/redundant.

1. How did you hear about this job?
2. Would you accept part-time employment?
3. Do you have a driver's license?
4. Which shift would you prefer?
5. Are you willing to work overtime?

6. What are your career goals?
7. Would you like to go back to school?
8. Why did you apply for this job?
9. Do you have any experience related to this job?
10. What makes you think you can handle this job?
11. Why did you leave your last job?
12. Have you ever been terminated during a probationary period?
13. How many jobs have you had in the last five years?
14. Describe your responsibilities in your previous job.
15. Do you have any hobbies?
16. Which of your job duties were your favorite?
17. Tell me your strongest characteristics.
18. If you didn't understand instructions that your supervisor gave you, what would you do?
19. How do you think you would react if you had a job with a lot of pressure?
20. What kind of supervisor would you like to work with?
21. What are your shortcomings?
22. Do you think that the salary we are offering is fair?

An applicant can also ask questions about the job's duties or benefits, which generally indicates interest in staying with the company if hired.

1. How big is this company?
2. What are the working hours? Are there different shifts?
3. Is there training available on the job?
4. What kinds of products or services do you provide?
5. What is the salary? How is it paid?
6. Is there any overtime or work on the weekends?
7. Are there benefits?
8. What are the duties and responsibilities of this job?
9. Is there room for advancement in the company?
10. Are you an Equal Opportunity Employer?

141

F. Application for a Social Security Number

Print in black or dark blue ink or use typewriter.			

1 Print Full Name you will use in work or business	(First)	(Middle)	(Last)

2 Print Full Name Given You at Birth	6 Your Date of Birth	(Month) (Day) (Year)

3 Place of Birth (City) (County) (State)	7 Your Present Age (Age on last birthday)

4 Mother's Full Name at Her Birth (Her Maiden Name)	8 Your Sex ☐ Male ☐ Female

8 Father's Full Name (Regardless of living or dead)	9 Your Color or Race ☐ White ☐ Black ☐ Other

10 Have you ever before applied for or had a United States Social Security, Railroad, or Tax Account Number?   ☐ No   ☐ Yes   ☐ Don't Know

(If "yes," print state in which you applied and Social Security Number if known.)   (City)   (State)   (Zip Code)

11 Your Mailing Address (Number and Street, Apt. No., P.O. Box, or Rural Route)   (City)   (State)   (Zip Code)

12 Today's Date	14 NOTICE: Whoever, with intent to falsify his or someone else's true identity, willfully furnishes or causes to be furnished false information in applying for a Social Security number is subject to a fine of not more than $1,000 or imprisonment for up to 1 year, or both.
13 Telephone Number	Sign Your Name Here (Do Not Print)

IX. Problem Solving

Mike and Barry work as busboys at a large, popular restaurant. They have been working together for a couple of years, and although they're not close friends, they still know each other pretty well. Mike has noticed a change of behavior ever since Barry broke up with his girlfriend. Barry has been drinking the leftover wine in glasses left on the table, and every night he leaves the restaurant almost drunk. Mike stopped him one night and asked him why he had a lot of silverware in his pocket. Barry said, "It's just a little. A big rich place like this won't miss it." Then one day the boss called all the workers together and said that a lot of silverware was missing and that he was going to subtract the cost from all of their salaries. What should Mike do?

A. What is the problem?_____

_____

_____

_____

B. What are all the possible solutions?_____

_____

_____

_____

C. What is the best solution? _____

_____

_____

_____

UNIT 7

BANKING

It seems as if money makes the world go around. Banks offer services that can provide not only safety and convenience, but also accurate record keeping of a person's cash. They offer a convenient way to pay bills with checks and to help out when one wants to get a loan. This unit presents those necessary aspects of English in the subject area of banking.

Objectives

Competencies:
Checks
Bank Forms
Credit Cards

Structure:
Prepositions
Participles

Pronunciation:
short u (ŭ)
short u (ŭ) / short a (ă)
J / SH and SH / CH

144

I. Vocabulary

A. Banking

1. cash
2. currency
3. coins
4. bill
5. teller
6. window
7. line
8. interest
9. interest rate
10. check
11. checking account
12. balance
13. balance a checkbook
14. savings account
15. deposit (slip)
16. withdraw
   (withdrawal slip)
17. pass book
18. minimum balance
19. service charge
20. safe deposit box
21. loan
22. brochure
23. insufficient funds
24. overdraw
25. drive-up window
26. automatic 24-hour teller
27. money order
28. bank by mail
29. bank statement
30. annual statement
31. quarterly statement
32. establish credit
33. endorse

Exercise V-1: Fill in the blanks with the appropriate word from the vocabulary above. Not all words are used.

Every Friday I go to the bank to get _____ for the weekend. I always wait in a long _____, but it's not long before the _____ smiles and calls me to the _____. Sometimes I change money from another country, which is called foreign _____. If I have too many _____, I change them for paper money. Most of the time I go to the bank to put money in my savings _____. For this I need to fill out a _____ slip. I only take out or _____ money when it's absolutely necessary.

Last month I changed banks. I read about the _____ rates in their _____. I wanted to write checks, like paying the telephone _____ every month, so I asked to start a _____ account. The teller said that there was no _____ balance or _____ charge, so I deposited my money. She asked me, "Would you be interested in a _____ _____ box to keep your valuables in?"

I answered, "No, thank you, but I would like to know more about _____ orders."

She gave me another brochure to read. She said that I didn't have to come inside the bank every time because I could use the _____-_____ _____ , or bank by _____ , or use the _____ , which is open 24 hours. She said that I would receive a _____ statement every month and a _____ statement every three months plus an _____ statement at the end of the year for my savings account. I asked her what "insufficient funds" meant, and she explained that it is when you _____ from your account.

Next week my brother is going to write me a _____ because he owes me some money. I'll write my name on the back and _____ it. I'll be spending my money quickly, mostly for groceries and clothes. Next year I will ask for a _____ to buy a car, but I must _____ _____ for myself first. Every time I look in my savings account, I feel a little discouraged.

II. Getting Started

A.

B.

Picture A

1. Describe what's in the picture.
2. What are the advantages and disadvantages of using an automatic bank teller?
3. Are there automatic tellers in your native country?

Picture B

1. Describe what's in the picture.
2. What are the disadvantages of using the services inside the bank?
3. What are some differences between banks here and your native country?

Pictures A and B

1. Describe those things that are the same and those things that are different in both pictures.
2. Louise is just moving into a city. She wants to set up a checking and savings account in a bank. She's a very careful and successful businesswoman. What do you think she'll do?

146

III. Conversation

A.

C = Customer   T = Teller

C: Hello, I want to start a checking and savings account.

T: Very good. Just fill out this application and you'll be ready to start your account. How much do you want to deposit in your checking account?

C: Let's see . . . How about $300?

T: That's fine. And your savings account?

C. Oh, $1000.

T: Good. Now will this be a cash deposit?

C. Yes, it will.

T: OK, here is your checkbook and this is your savings passbook. More checks will come in the mail with the style you want and your name and address on them. You can choose from these. And also, there's no charge on the first 200 checks.

C: I'd like these with the scenic pictures on them.

T: I'll make sure that you get them. I hope that you enjoy all the services of our bank. There's no minimum balance on your checking account.

C: Thank you. Next time I'll probably use the drive-up window. I don't like to take my baby into the bank.

T: Well, thank you and if there's anything I can do for you, let me know.

B.

GS = Grandson   GP = Grandpa

GS: Hey, Grandpa, do you want to go to the bank with me? I have a few checks to deposit.

GP: No thanks. I'm busy with a crossword puzzle. And anyway, I don't like banks. I don't trust them.

GS: Why?

GP: Aw, those bankers with all their fancy interest rates just get rich off the hard-working people's money.

GS: You don't really believe that, do you, Grandpa?

GP: I surely do.

GS: Well then, what do you do with your money?

GP: I keep it in a secret place. And I'm not going to tell you!

C.

1. Oh, no, the bank's closed. I thought it was open until six o'clock.
2. On Friday it is, but today's Thursday. If you have an automatic teller card, you can use it to withdraw up to $200 or make a deposit.

1. I just got one of those cards in the mail but I haven't used it yet.
2. It's pretty easy. Just put your card in, enter your special number, and follow the instructions.

1. It sounds easy enough.
2. They're very convenient machines when they're working.

1. Do they have many problems?
2. Sometimes they have to close down, but usually they're pretty good.

1. No matter how convenient it is, I still miss the smiles of the real tellers.
2. Yeah, that's the one drawback of a computer.

Dialogue Puzzle: With a partner fill in the appropriate responses or questions in the spaces below, then practice and read to the rest of the class.

1. Is the bank open today?
2. _____

1. Who do I talk to about getting a loan?
2. _____

1. _____
2. That's a lot of money to ask for? What are you planning to buy?

1. _____
2. I'm sure you could find a real nice one at a much cheaper price.

1. Where can I look?
2. _____

1. Do you think it's wise to take out a loan there?
2. _____

Discussion: Answer the following questions about things talked about in the previous conversations.

1. Where do you (or a friend or relative) do your banking?
2. How often do you go there and what kind of services do you have?
3. What is your opinion of loans and credit in the United States?

IV. Reading

A. Vocabulary

get out of	competent	procedures	windshield
errands	instead	get	takes care of
drives off	confused	yell	loading zone
pass the time	shrugged	reward	recommend

B. Reading

Chris Wong drove with his new license for the first time since coming to the United States from Taiwan six months ago. He stopped in front of the bank and hurried in because he had a lot of errands to do. He needed to make a few deposits in his checking account and also to get about sixty dollars in cash for the weekend.

The line was long. The man in front of him explained that many people got their social security checks and that's why it was so crowded. Chris read some brochures to pass the time.

When Chris got to the window, the teller was friendly and competent, so he took care of his business quickly and left the bank. As he was leaving, however, he noticed a young woman in front of the automatic teller looking confused. She shrugged her shoulders and scratched her head, and said to herself out loud, "I don't understand this dumb machine."

Chris stopped and offered to help her. She said OK and then he explained the procedures.

"Great, I get it," she said. "Thanks."

Chris started to leave but before he reached his car, he heard her yell. He went back and she told him how she pushed the button for forty dollars but only twenty came out. Chris recommended that she report it right away to one of the employees inside the bank. She smiled and thanked him again.

When Chris got to his car, he saw a paper on his windshield. He thought it was an advertisement but instead it was a ticket. He had parked in a loading zone. He felt upset as he drove off. What a reward for helping someone out, he thought to himself.

C. Exercises

1. Write these sentences in the correct sequence of the story, using a 1 for what came first all the way to 7 as last.

    _____ a. The young woman yelled.

    _____ b. Chris found the ticket on his windshield.

    _____ c. Chris got his driver's license.

    _____ d. A man explained why the line was long.

    _____ e. Chris left Taiwan.

    _____ f. Chris looked through some of the bank's brochures.

    _____ g. The bank teller was nice to Chris.

149

2. Write *true* or *false*.

_____a. Chris got here a little over a year ago.

_____b. Chris was in a hurry.

_____c. The bank was crowded because the next day was a holiday.

_____d. The bank teller who waited on Chris was efficient.

_____e. Chris knew how to work the automatic teller.

_____f. The automatic teller didn't make a mistake.

_____g. Chris didn't care about the ticket.

3. Vocabulary: Put the vocabulary words from Section A (page 149) in the blank spaces.

a. When the teacher asked him the question, he just _____ his shoulders and looked _____ .

b. "Do you _____ it?" he asked after he told the joke.

c. They _____ the house in a hurry.

d. I _____ that you try another bank with better service.

e. There was $1000 _____ for the capture of the criminal.

f. The truck parked in the _____ _____ and unloaded several boxes.

g. Maria always gets in her car and _____ without cleaning her _____ .

h. Her son _____ any _____ that have to be done.

i. _____ of reading the _____ of the court, he'll _____ watching TV.

j. Don't _____ at that secretary. She's quite _____ .

V. Structure

| Prepositions |

A preposition is a word that shows the relationship between a noun or pronoun and another word in a sentence.

> Karen walked   <u>to</u>   the park.
> <u>in</u>
> <u>across</u>
> <u>by</u>

In this example, the different prepositions show different relationships between the person walking and the park.

Prepositions are like mosquitoes: They are small and always bothersome. Some come in two-word verbs like this:

> I will <u>wait</u> <u>for</u> you here tomorrow morning.

They also come in special expressions, like this:

> He should notify his bank <u>in</u> the <u>case</u> <u>of</u> an error.

By reading and listening to English while paying attention to the use of prepositions, you can gradually learn them.

The principal prepositions are:

<u>aboard</u>
> They hurried <u>aboard</u> the plane.

<u>about</u>
> The bank manager talked <u>about</u> the money market account.
> She walked <u>about</u> the lobby.

<u>above</u>
> There is a leak in the ceiling <u>above</u> you.
> The temperature is <u>above</u> normal.

<u>across</u>
> The teller walked <u>across</u> the room.
> We heard the noise <u>across</u> the street.

<u>after</u>
> The police went <u>after</u> the bank robbers.
> They went home <u>after</u> depositing the checks.

<u>against</u>
> She leaned <u>against</u> the door.
> He fought bravely <u>against</u> the disease.
> He threw the ball <u>against</u> the wall.

along

The boat sailed along the coast.

They planted the flowers along the driveway.

amid (amidst)

She continued sorting the checks amid all the noise.

They had a picnic amidst the beautiful trees.

among

Your letter was just one among thousands.

He sat among friends.

around

Their family traveled around the state.

He walked around the corner.

at

Someone's at the door.

The plane'll leave at 3:30.

Don't yell at me!

I was only looking at TV.

They're at work now.

before

Kevin spoke to us before the meeting.

He stopped before the familiar house.

The defendant appeared before the judge.

The matter was before the committee.

below

Their apartment is below yours.

The temperature is below normal for this time of year.

beneath

There was a sock beneath the blanket.

beside

His safe deposit box is beside hers.

I don't have anything to do beside this.

besides

There are two more bank statements besides this.

between

The hammock stretched between the trees.

You can come to my house between 7:00 and 8:00.

What's the difference between the two accounts?

beyond

The lake is just beyond the hills.

He stayed beyond the hospital's visiting hours.

The nuclear accident was beyond belief.

by

Mary's house is <u>by</u> the bank.

We went <u>by</u> his house the other day.

I'll return from the bank <u>by</u> five o'clock.

The book was <u>by</u> Ernest Hemingway.

The insects came <u>by</u> the millions.

It's a ten <u>by</u> twelve-foot room.

They came <u>by</u> car and were paid <u>by</u> the hour.

but

Everyone came <u>but</u> him.

concerning

The speech <u>concerning</u> nuclear disarmament was excellent.

considering

She did very well <u>considering</u> the difficulties.

down

They live just <u>down</u> the street.

He hurried <u>down</u> the stairs.

despite

They had a good time <u>despite</u> the bad weather.

during

We talked about discrimination <u>during</u> the coffee break.

except

Everyone got a brochure <u>except</u> me.

for

The land here is flat <u>for</u> several miles.

The warranty is good <u>for</u> 90 days.

They are voting <u>for</u> safer laws.

The check was <u>for</u> $500.

He left <u>for</u> home.

Martin is asking <u>for</u> a loan.

He bought flowers <u>for</u> his wife.

I know it <u>for</u> a fact.

They're selling the house <u>for</u> $175,000.

I have an appointment <u>for</u> two o'clock.

I walk <u>for</u> exercise.

There's a need <u>for</u> improvement.

from

My house is two blocks <u>from</u> the savings and loan.

The sale is <u>from</u> noon until five.

He took some change <u>from</u> his pocket.

Paper comes <u>from</u> trees.

She got a letter <u>from</u> John.

<u>in</u>

The money is <u>in</u> the checking account.

The boat's <u>in</u> the room.

I'll be back <u>in</u> an hour.

They arrived <u>in</u> the morning.

The book was <u>in</u> English.

They shouted <u>in</u> anger.

<u>In</u> my opinion he'll be <u>in</u> business a long time.

<u>inside</u>

Her jewelry is <u>inside</u> the box.

<u>into</u>

He reached <u>into</u> the drawer and got the key.

<u>like</u>

She looks <u>like</u> her mother.

<u>near</u>

He wants to sell his house that is <u>near</u> the polluting plant.

It's getting <u>near</u> closing time.

<u>of</u>

Mr. Kitson died <u>of</u> cancer.

Have you read the poems <u>of</u> Edgar Allen Poe?

I borrowed one <u>of</u> his bikes.

She looked through several pages <u>of</u> his passbook.

The State <u>of</u> Nevada has informed them <u>of</u> the problem.

They live north <u>of</u> the city.

I have a bag <u>of</u> coins.

<u>off</u>

The paper blew <u>off</u> the desk.

He lived <u>off</u> his father's inheritance.

They took his name <u>off</u> the list.

The policeman is <u>off</u> duty now.

<u>on</u>

My aunt left the keys <u>on</u> the table.

Karen felt nervous <u>on</u> the first day of work.

The movie is based <u>on</u> his life story.

She's <u>on</u> the committee.

He was <u>on</u> TV last night.

Your cousins lived <u>on</u> fruits and vegetables.

They're <u>on</u> a trip.

Tom shined the light <u>on</u> it.

Herb wrote an essay <u>on</u> peace.

<u>onto</u>

He carefully put the book <u>onto</u> the shelf.

out

> Mark walked <u>out</u> the door.
>
> The juice came <u>out</u> of the bottle.

outside

> They lived <u>outside</u> the city limits.

over

> The plane flew <u>over</u> the peninsula.
>
> They talked <u>over</u> dinner.
>
> The company has been making money <u>over</u> the last ten years.
>
> It cost <u>over</u> $100.
>
> He chose fruit <u>over</u> cake.
>
> What did you do <u>over</u> the weekend?
>
> They had a quarrel <u>over</u> politics.

past

> Sara walked <u>past</u> the automatic 24-hour teller.
>
> It's ten <u>past</u> nine.

per

> It costs $60 <u>per</u> day to stay there for single occupancy.

regarding

> We listened to the information <u>regarding</u> service charges.

since

> He's been here <u>since</u> two o'clock.

through

> The nail went <u>through</u> the wall.
>
> The ball sailed <u>through</u> the air.
>
> The diplomat spoke <u>through</u> an interpreter.
>
> He'll stay <u>through</u> winter.
>
> The bank is open Monday <u>through</u> Friday.

throughout

> The song is number one <u>throughout</u> the country.

till, until

> The guarantee is valid <u>until</u> the end of the year.
>
> He won't be back <u>till</u> five.

to

> He went <u>to</u> Texas last week <u>to</u> see his sister.
>
> It's ten <u>to</u> nine now.
>
> It seems fine <u>to</u> me.
>
> She remained true <u>to</u> her beliefs.
>
> That's all there is <u>to</u> it.

The odds were 17 <u>to</u> 1 on the race horse.

I couldn't find the key <u>to</u> my house.

The contest is open <u>to</u> everyone.

The stocks fell <u>to</u> an all-time low.

He left his estate <u>to</u> his son.

<u>toward(s)</u>

They drove <u>toward</u> the border.

Bob and Karen arrived <u>toward</u> evening.

They are making steps <u>towards</u> peace.

<u>under</u>

There is a tunnel <u>under</u> the river.

He drove <u>under</u> the bridge.

She wore a sweater <u>under</u> her coat.

He's <u>under</u> age.

She was <u>under</u> oath.

<u>Under</u> the circumstances it was all we could do.

The country was very prosperous <u>under</u> his rule.

<u>underneath</u>

The calculator is <u>underneath</u> the paper.

<u>up</u>

The mountain climber struggled <u>up</u> the peak.

He's trying to move <u>up</u> in the company.

They live just <u>up</u> the road.

They paddled in the boat <u>up</u> the river.

<u>via</u>

He came here from New York <u>via</u> Chicago.

I sent the letter <u>via</u> air mail.

<u>with</u>

He argued <u>with</u> his friend.

The artist mixed blue <u>with</u> yellow.

He has been <u>with</u> the firm for twenty years.

She was pleased <u>with</u> her birthday present.

I'm <u>with</u> you there.

It's all right <u>with</u> me.

The man with the brown hair spoke <u>with</u> pride.

<u>With</u> all his boasting about being brave he's still afraid.

<u>With</u> that remark, he left.

I played tennis <u>with</u> Roberto.

He competes <u>with</u> the best.

He played <u>with</u> the toy.

within

His house is <u>within</u> a mile of the factory.

The lawyer will arrive <u>within</u> an hour.

The matter is not <u>within</u> our jurisdiction.

without

He entered the room <u>without</u> his friend.

She's <u>without</u> a credit card now.

He passed by <u>without</u> even saying hello.

Exercise S-1: Write in a correct preposition. Note that some may have more than one possible answer.

1. The captain invited us _____ the ship.

2. They heard the noise _____ the street.

3. He leaned _____ the wall.

4. The customer was one _____ thousands there.

5. Smoke came out _____ the windows.

6. Why is he so angry _____ everyone?

7. The custodian found some gum _____ the desks.

8. The test scores were far _____ average.

9. The park is _____ that turn in the road.

10. Is anyone else coming _____ you?

11. The logs floated _____ the river.

12. Some birds fly only _____ night.

13. He stands _____ his statement.

14. The hotel is five miles _____ the airport.

15. The little kid is really smart _____ his age.

16. He spoke _____ a whisper.

17. The locket is made _____ gold.

18. The secretary took his name _____ the list.

19. I'll be _____ my way now; see you _____ five o'clock.

20. The bottle _____ the shelf is _____ your reach. Don't worry, I'll get it _____ you.

21. He wore a raincoat _____ his nice jacket.

22. The boy threw the eraser _____ the room.

23. Her fame spread _____ the country.

24. My friend stayed up _____ midnight last night.

25. The beach was directly _____ the cliff.

26. The meat costs $3.79 _____ pound.
27. _____ coffee break, she wrote a letter _____
English.
28. The student wrote _____ a piece _____
paper _____ that desk _____ a pencil.
29. Susan was so sick that Mary went _____ her
_____ the movies.
30. _____ the cabin it's snowing. _____
this room it's warm.

Exercise S-2: Write your own sentences using these prepositions.

1. (during) _____
2. (through) _____
3. (along) _____
4. (among) _____
5. (above) _____

Participles

A participle has the form of a verb, but it acts like an adjective, always describing a noun or pronoun.

The <u>hurrying</u> customer dropped his deposit slip.

(Verb form: to <u>hurry</u>. Adjective action: It describes the noun, <u>customer</u>.)

There are two kinds of participles, present and past.

A. Present Participle

The present participle has the present form of the verb plus -ing. It shows action that takes place at the same time as the main verb.

    verb: cry   present participle: crying

      He could hear the crying baby.

    verb: bark   present participle: barking

      A barking dog bothered him.

Exercise S-3: Form participles from the verbs in parentheses and write in the spaces, using the present form.

1. (excite) It was an _____ movie.
2. (disturb) His _____ remarks were in the newspaper.
3. (smile/whistle) _____ and _____, the man left the bank.

4. (work) She's a hard-_____ teller.

5. (talk) I don't like fast-_____ salespeople.

6. (interest) Margaret likes _____ stories.

Exercise: Make your own sentence using present participles from the verb and noun.

Example:

(scream/teenagers) The concert was full of <u>screaming</u> <u>teenagers.</u>

1. (shock/news) _____

2. (open/presentation) _____

3. (amuse/story) _____

B. Past Participle:

The past participle is the third principal form of the verb (walk-walked-WALKED or break-broke-BROKEN). It shows action that takes place before the action of the main verb.

He gave her a <u>sealed</u> envelope.

I received the <u>forwarded</u> letter.

The <u>broken</u> chair is in the other room.

Exercise S-4: Form your own sentence using past participles from the verb and noun.

1. (endorse) Did he find an _____ check?

2. (vanish) The book is about many _____ civilizations.

3. (arrive) They greeted the recently- _____ immigrants.

4. (address) Be sure to include a self- _____ envelope.

5. (water/give) _____ and _____ care, the plant grew tall.

6. (balance) It's already a _____ checkbook.

7. (know) She's a well-_____ actress.

Exercise S-5: Make your own sentences using past participles from the verb and noun.

Example:

(approve/application) He received an approved application.

1. (complete/form) _____

2. (retire/bank manager) _____

3. (return/package) _____

VI. Composition

Exercise C-1: Write the words of your choice, according to the description below each space. After you finish, let your teacher correct and then read aloud.

In the United States the system of banking is _____ .
                                            (adjective)
Banks are necessary when a person has to _____ . The
                                        (verb)
closest bank to where I live is _____ . The
                               (name of bank)
best thing about banks here is _____ while
                               (bank service)
the worst thing is _____ . I think that it is
                    (bank service)
_____ to get a loan from a bank. The interest rates
(difficult/easy)
at banks are _____ .
             (adjective or number)
The biggest bank in my native country is _____
                                         (name of bank)
located in _____ . The difference between banks in
           (city)
my native country and banks here is _____
                                    (sentence)
_____ . The working hours of banks in my native

country are _____ . The service in these banks
            (times)
is _____ . Banks are closed on _____ .
   (adjective)   (days)
Loans are _____ to get.
          (difficult/easy)
Banks keep their money secure by using _____
                                       (ways to keep banks safe)
_____ . There are _____ bank
                             (more/fewer)
robberies in my native country than here. Persons rob banks because

_____ .
(sentence)

VII. Pronunciation

A. Vowel:

short u or (ŭ)

1. b<u>u</u>t	2. c<u>ou</u>ntry	3. tr<u>ou</u>ble
m<u>o</u>ney	f<u>u</u>nds	tr<u>u</u>st
al<u>o</u>ng	d<u>oe</u>s	bl<u>oo</u>d

4. Her <u>o</u>ther s<u>o</u>n sh<u>u</u>t th<u>e</u> tr<u>u</u>nk s<u>o</u>me time <u>a</u>go.

5. S<u>o</u>me<u>o</u>ne s<u>u</u>ddenly r<u>u</u>shed to buy <u>a</u> m<u>o</u>ney order.

Contrasts:

short u (ŭ) / short a (ă)

6. hut/hat	7. but/bat	8. cut/cat
stub/stab	mud/mad	crush/crash
tug/tag	much/match	run/ran

B. Consonants

J / SH and SH / CH

1. gin/shin
   jade/shade
   jeep/sheep
   jingle/shingle

2. share/chair
   sheet/cheat
   dishes/ditches
   cash/catch

3. She's washing the dishes and catching up on the chores.

4. Jack shaved in the shack while Marge sat in the shade.

VIII. Life Skills

A. Checks

You have a few bills to pay today. You owe Jackson's Department Store $61.87 for some clothes you bought, $134.55 to Star Telephone Company for all those long distance calls you made back home, and $20 to your friend Kathy Riley, who lent you the cash for groceries the other night.

Write checks for these payments and keep a record of it in your checkbook. (The first check has explanations of what each line is for.)

1. Date

2. Who you are paying

3. Amount in numbers

4. Amount in writing

5. To remind you how you spent it

6. Signature

```
                                                    NO. 277
                    1.
                    _____ 19_____    11-35/1210
PAY TO THE      2.                                  3.
ORDER OF _____ $_____
4. _____DOLLARS

FIRST STANDARD BANK
Smallville, U.S.A.
        5.                        6.
Memo _____    _____
:0310000569:0101:01453:54328
```

```
                                                    NO. 278
                    _____ 19_____    11-35/1210
PAY TO THE
ORDER OF _____ $_____
_____DOLLARS

FIRST STANDARD BANK
Smallville, U.S.A.

Memo _____    _____
:0310000569:0101:01453:54328
```

```
                                                    NO. 279
                    _____ 19_____   11-35/1210
PAY TO THE
ORDER OF_____ $_____
_____DOLLARS

FIRST STANDARD BANK
Smallville, U.S.A.

Memo _____      _____
:0310000569:0101:01453:54328
```

This is your checkbook. Write in the previous payments and figure out your balance, which is $1000 before these checks.

		RECORD ALL CHARGES OR CREDITS THAT AFFECT YOUR ACCOUNT				
NUMBER	DATE	DESCRIPTION OF TRANSACTION	PAYMENT/CREDIT (–)	FEE (IF ANY)	DEPOSIT/CREDIT (+)	BALANCE

B. Bank Forms

You have two checks, one with the ABA (American Banker's Association) number 11-35 for the amount of $65.37 and the other with ABA 90-1936 for $30.00. You want to deposit them in your checking account and keep $25 for cash. Compete the form.

```
        For Deposit to the Account of      | CASH  CURRENCY |
                    YOU                     |            COIN |
                Anywhere, U.S.A.            | List Checks Singly |
                                            |                 |
                                            |                 |
        DATE_____ 19_____  | Total From Other Side |
                                            |                 |
        _____  | TOTAL           |
        SIGN HERE FOR LESS CASH IN TELLER'S PRESENCE | Less Cash Received |
        FIRST STANDARD BANK                 | NET DEPOSIT     |
        :031000569:0101:01453:54328
```

Mrs. Lee, who lives at 783 Grant Ave., Los Angeles, California, wants to take $300 out of her savings to buy her husband a birthday gift. Her account number at this bank is 798-1-23265465. How would she fill out this form?

```
┌────────────────────────────────────────────────────────────────────┐
│                 FIRST STANDARD NATIONAL BANK                         │
│                      Savings Withdrawal                              │
│   11-53/1210                                  Date:____/____/____    │
│   └──┴──┴──┘   └──┴──┴──┴──┴──┴──┴──┴──┴──┴──┴──┴──┴──┴──┴──┘        │
│   BRANCH        ACCOUNT NO.                                          │
│   Received from My Account with First Standard Bank_____ │
│                                                    DOLLARS/CENTS     │
│   _____ DOLLARS  │
│   ┌───────────────────┐  Signature _____  │
│   │  BANK USE ONLY    │  Address _____  │
│   │  Cash   CC   TR   │          _____  │
│   └───────────────────┘  :5065:000:                                 │
└────────────────────────────────────────────────────────────────────┘
```

C. Credit Cards

```
┌──────────────────────────────────────────┐
│          STANDARD BANK CARD                │
├──────────────────────────────────────────┤
│                 T I S A                    │
├──────────────────────────────────────────┤
│        743   349   685   98   01           │
│   Maria Gibson          Good Thru 3/89     │
└──────────────────────────────────────────┘
```

Exercise L-1:

1. Whose credit card is this? _____

2. What is the renewal date? _____

3. What is the card's identification number?_____

4. What would this person do if she lost this card? _____

   _____

```
┌─────────────────────────────────────────────────────────────────┐
│ Standard Bank Card Statement          T I S A                     │
│ Account Number: 743 349 685 98 01                                 │
│                                                                   │
│ Closing Date    Mimimum Payment    New Balance    Payment Due Date│
│ 10-30-89          $25.00            $486.32         11-24-89      │
│                                                                   │
│ Annual Percentage Rate: 18%    Amount Enclosed $_____ │
│                                                                   │
│                                Make Check Payable to:             │
│        Maria Gibson            TISA                               │
│        893 Main St.            P.O. Box 456                        │
│        Grassroots, USA         Los Angeles, CA 90054              │
└─────────────────────────────────────────────────────────────────┘
```

Exercise L-2: Answer the questions about the above bank card statement.

1. How much does Maria owe for the last month on her credit card?

   _____

2. By what date does she have to pay it? _____

3. Does she have to pay the whole payment now? _____

4. What's the annual interest rate? _____

5. Maria calls her mother and asks to borrow the money to pay off this bill because she doesn't have the money. Her mother doesn't like credit cards and always pays with cash. What do you think her mother would say to her?_____

   _____

   _____

IX. Problem Solving

David and Terry just got married and never had a credit card before. Terry does most of the buying because David hates to go shopping. Terry hates going to the bank to get cash so she asked David if they could get a credit card. David said OK. After a few months David received the credit card bill and noticed it was very high. He warned Terry to be careful. The next month it was even higher. David's worried that they are spending too much money for what they earn, and Terry insists that she is just buying what they need.

A. What is the problem?_____

   _____

B. What are all the possible solutions?_____

   _____

C. What is the best solution? _____

   _____

UNIT 8

HOUSING

In the United States housing procedures and regulations may differ from state to state, from city to city. The need to find affordable, suitable housing is high on the list of basic needs for the newcomer here, who often has to find a place to stay before he knows the appropriate language to meet this critical need. This unit will provide students with the English needed to find that comfortable home.

Objectives

Competencies:
Classified Ads
Rental Agreements
Rental Housing Problems
Utility Bills
Home Energy Conservation

Structure:
Prepositional Phrases
Past Perfect and Past Perfect Continuous

Pronunciation:
short o ($\breve{o}$)
short o ($\breve{o}$) / short u ($\breve{u}$)
J / CH and J / Y

I. Vocabulary

A. House

<u>Rooms:</u> living room, front room, dining room, kitchen, bedroom, study, den, family room, recreation room, utility room, hall, stairs, laundry room, storeroom, closet, bathroom, attic, basement.

<u>Kinds of houses:</u> duplex, mansion, ranch, farm, cabin, cottage, chalet, mobile home.

<u>Around the house:</u> garage, porch, backyard, fence, front, foundation, driveway, roof, balcony, chimney, fireplace, electrical outlets, sewage, water/gas hookups.

<u>Materials:</u> steel, cement, wood, brick, rock, stone, aluminum, copper, glass, asbestos, sheetrock.

<u>Jobs:</u> realtor (real estate), architect, contractor, construction worker, bricklayer, carpenter, welder, plumber, electrician, roofer, painter.

<u>Miscellaneous:</u>

1. neighborhood
2. community
3. block
4. home, dwelling, residence
5. resident, occupant
6. owner
7. floor, level, story
8. lot (residential, commercial)
9. design, floor plans, blueprints
10. subdivision
11. factory-built home, tract home
12. purchase offer
13. down payment
14. contract
15. mortgage
16. property taxes
17. appraise/appraisal
18. zoning laws
19. market value
20. deed/title
21. permit
22. additions
23. remodeling
24. estimate
25. insulation

B. Apartment

<u>Kinds:</u> studio, flat, duplex, high-rise, townhouse, condominium.

<u>Miscellaneous:</u>

1. landlord, landlady
2. manager
3. renter, tenant
4. maintenance person
5. rental agreement
6. lease
7. rent
8. advance rent
9. last month's rent
10. deposit
11. reference
12. cleaning fee
13. compliant
14. eviction
15. utilities
16. sublet
17. rent control

C. Abbreviations in Want Ads

1. AEK — all electric kitchen
2. appt — appointment
3. apt — apartment
4. air cond — air conditioning
5. avail — available
6. BA — bathroom
7. beaut — beautiful
8. BR — bedroom
9. bldg — building
10. balc — balcony
11. cpts — carpets
12. ctr — center
13. conv — convenient
14. decor — decorated
15. delx/lux — deluxe/luxurious
16. drps — drapes
17. dep — deposit
18. enc — enclosed
19. eves — evenings
20. exc — excellent
21. frplc — fireplace
22. frwy — freeway
23. furn — furnished
24. garb — garbage
25. gar — garage
26. ht — heat
27. immac — immaculate
28. gd — good
29. incl — included
30. lge — large
31. lndry — laundry
32. loc — location
33. micro — microwave
34. min — minimum
35. mo — month
36. mgr — manager
37. nr — near
38. opt — optional
39. pvt — private
40. refrig — refrigerator
41. refs — references
42. redec — redecorated
43. spac — spacious
44. sec — security
45. trans — transportation
46. utils — utilities
47. w/w cpt — wall-to-wall carpet
48. W-D — washer, dryer

II. Getting Started

A.

B.

Picture A

1. Describe what's in the picture.
2. How much would a house like that one cost to buy?
3. How are houses different in your native country?

Picture B

1. Describe what's in the picture.
2. How much would an apartment like one in this complex cost to rent?
3. How are apartments different in your native country?

Pictures A and B

1. Point out those things that are the same and those things that are different in these pictures.
2. Monique and her husband are renting an apartment. One of their neighbors makes a lot of noise late at night, which disturbs their sleep. What should they do?

III. Conversation

A.

1. Houses here are very expensive.
2. You're not kidding. It takes a fortune to buy one.

1. The prices of homes and the value of property keep going up.
2. My cousin bought a house two months ago and he's happy with it.

1. I guess you have to be careful when you buy a house. You have to check out everything.
2. Yes, you have to check the plumbing and the electric wiring and also see if there's any pest or rodent problem. And of course the location and the design and how it's built.

1. I think the space inside is very important. What kind of house did your cousin buy?
2. A tract home in the suburbs. It's a new but friendly neighborhood.

1. Sounds pretty good. Well, see you later.
2. Bye. And good luck with your house hunting.

B.

1. Did you have any luck finding an apartment?
2. No, I saw one in the classified ads that was in my price range, but when I checked it out, I changed my mind.

1. What was the matter with it?
2. It wasn't big enough and the utilities weren't included.

1. It took me a long time to find a good apartment. They're pretty expensive around here but with a little time I found one that I liked.
2. I liked the location of this apartment. It was close to my work and a good shopping center. There are many things to consider before you rent, though.
1. Yes, you've got to be careful before you go through all the trouble of moving in. Well, good luck and don't give up.
2. Sure, I'm planning on continuing my apartment search. Tomorrow I'm going to check out the advertising cards on the bulletin boards of the local supermarkets.

C.

1. I just talked to my landlord.
2. What was the matter?
1. My heater hasn't been working very well and my kitchen sink faucet is leaking.
2. Was he cooperative with you?
1. Yes, he said he would have everything fixed up in no time.
2. That's great. Sometimes it takes a long time to get something taken care of. How long have you been renting there?
1. Quite a while. The first thing I did when I moved in was to make friends with the manager.
2. Not a bad idea. The next time that I talk to someone about renting an apartment, I'll recommend doing that.

Dialogue Puzzle: With a partner fill in the appropriate responses or questions in the spaces of the dialogue below, then practice and read to the rest of the class.

1. My family and I just got here in the United States.
2. _____

1. Yes, we would like to live here permanently. We like this area.
2. _____

1. _____
2. How much do you pay for it?

1. _____
2. Is it very spacious inside?

1. Yes, it has two bedrooms and one large bathroom, a dining and living room and a big kitchen.
2. _____

1. We found it in an ad in the paper.
2. _____

169

Discussion: Answer the following questions about things talked about in the previous conversations.

1. Describe the house that you grew up in.
2. What was the best neighborhood you were ever in?
3. Who was the most thoughtful neighbor you ever had? The worst?
4. What's the most important consideration before a person buys a house?

IV. Reading

A. Vocabulary

condominium	environment	realtor
inconvenient	arrangement	split
furnished	swinging bachelor	steep
facilities	practical	ways
get in the way	utilities	bit
can't stand		

B. Reading

When Chris Wong first arrived in the United States, he lived with his uncle in a condominium that had a beautiful view of the city. This soon became an inconvenient arrangement, however, because the place wasn't very spacious, and besides, Chris's uncle was a swinging bachelor and Chris more often than not just got in the way. But since his uncle was also a realtor, it wasn't long before he found an apartment for Chris.

The apartment was a studio located in a noisy part of town. The landlord and the manager were very friendly and cooperative in fixing anything that went wrong. The studio was furnished and had wall-to-wall carpets. There were also a swimming pool and laundry facilities in the middle of the complex. The only thing that bothered Chris was that they allowed pets. One day one of the dogs bit him when he went to get his mail. There was a cat that always got into his room when the door was open, and the person next door had a pet snake. After a few months Chris decided to leave.

He found two other Chinese students to share the cost of renting a house in an area where the rents were very steep. They split the monthly expenditures and duties three ways. The house was big and had a nice garden. They had to pay the utilities themselves which sometimes ran pretty high, especially with their long distance calls back home and the high heating bills during the winter. Everything was fine there until they had a few parties. They made so much noise that all the neighbors complained to the owner of the house. After a while they had to leave.

Chris thought that the only place to live without any problems would be in the forest in a quiet, natural environment. That wasn't very practical, though. He finally found a pleasant apartment near his school where now he could concentrate on studying.

170

C. Exercises

1. Write these sentences in the correct time sequence, using a 1 for what happened first all the way to 7 as last.

_____ a. A dog bit Chris.

_____ b. After too many loud parties, the three students had to leave the house.

_____ c. Chris's uncle found an apartment for him.

_____ d. Chris arrived in the United States.

_____ e. Chris found two other students to share a house.

_____ f. Chris decided to leave the studio.

_____ g. Chris finally settled down in an apartment near his school.

2. Write _true_ or _false_.

_____ a. Chris's uncle lived in a condominium.

_____ b. Chris and his uncle got along very well.

_____ c. The manager of the studio wasn't cooperative.

_____ d. Chris liked pets.

_____ e. A snake is an unusual pet.

_____ f. The students divided their costs and responsibilities evenly.

_____ g. Living in the forest wasn't a practical idea for Chris.

3. Put the vocabulary words from Section A (page 170) in the spaces.

a. He _____ into the apple.

b. They have _____ the house with priceless antiques.

c. Does the stadium have adequate restroom _____?

d. It'll be very _____ for me to come now. I'm really busy.

e. The price of that _____ is quite steep.

f. The _____ aren't included in the monthly rent.

g. She _____ hamburgers: they upset her stomach.

h. Will that _____ _____ ever settle down and get married?

i. The child will only _____ while you're working.

j. The flower _____ was beautiful.

k. They are going to _____ the dinner bill four _____. Each will pay an equal amount.

l. The _____ can find you another home in a quieter _____ .

m. It won't be very _____ to take two cars. Why waste the gas?

V. Structure

> **Prepositional Phrases**

A. A prepositional phrase is a group of words with one or more prepositions that acts like a single preposition.

The landlord was <u>in favor of</u> making the improvements.

Here are some common prepositional phrases:

<u>according to</u>
They filled out the form <u>according to</u> the directions.

<u>by means of</u>
She gets around <u>by means of</u> a wheelchair.

<u>for the purpose of</u>
<u>For the purpose of</u> clarification, I'll repeat the instructions.

<u>in addition to</u>
The apartment has a pool <u>in addition to</u> the laundry facilities.

<u>in back of, in front of</u>
The garage is <u>in back of</u> the house.
He parked his mobile home <u>in front of</u> Rick's cabin.

<u>on account of</u>
They decided to move <u>on account of</u> the high rent.

<u>out of respect for</u>
The stores closed <u>out of respect for</u> the national holiday.

<u>regardless of</u>
Anyone can come <u>regardless of</u> age, sex or nationality.

<u>the matter with</u>
What's <u>the matter with</u> that tenant? He looks awfully pale.

<u>with the exception of</u>
Everyone was there <u>with the exception of</u> the manager.

Exercise S-1: Choose the appropriate prepositional phrases from above and write in the spaces.

1. They postponed the appointment _____ the new problems.

2. Anyone can apply for the job _____ previous experience or education.

172

3. Everyone remained quiet _____ the leader who had died.

4. He'll have ice cream _____ the pie.

B. Two-Word Verbs

Two-word verbs are verbs and prepositions (and occasionally other words like nouns and adjectives) that form special idioms which sometimes change the meaning of the original verb.

They <u>looked</u> <u>up</u> the word in the dictionary.

The verb "look" and the preposition "up" form a different meaning: to "find." Here are some other examples.

He <u>is</u> <u>afraid</u> <u>of</u> the operation.
You'll have to <u>wait</u> <u>for</u> the results.

Some two-word verbs can be separated when a pronoun is the object.

They <u>looked</u> <u>it</u> <u>up</u> in the dictionary.

There are many two-word verbs in English. Here are some of them:

<u>be</u> <u>different</u> <u>from</u>
A mansion <u>is</u> <u>different</u> <u>from</u> a cottage.

<u>be</u> <u>(nice/kind/polite/rude)</u> <u>to</u>
The realtor <u>was</u> <u>very</u> <u>polite</u> <u>to</u> me.

<u>be</u> <u>pleased</u> <u>with</u>
She <u>was</u> <u>pleased</u> <u>with</u> the new lease.

<u>be</u> <u>responsible</u> <u>for</u>
Who <u>was</u> <u>responsible</u> <u>for</u> the plumbing?

<u>be</u> <u>surprised</u> <u>at</u>
I <u>am</u> <u>surprised</u> <u>at</u> the amount of cement they used for the foundation.

<u>agree</u> <u>with,</u> <u>agree</u> <u>on</u>
The contractor <u>agreed</u> <u>with</u> the architect.
The two countries <u>agreed</u> <u>on</u> a new arms treaty.

<u>apologize</u> <u>for</u>
Will you <u>apologize</u> <u>for</u> causing such a mess?

<u>apply</u> <u>for</u>
He has <u>applied</u> <u>for</u> a new job.

<u>ask</u> <u>for</u>
When you call the real estate office, <u>ask</u> <u>for</u> Mrs. Harrison.

<u>care</u> <u>for,</u> <u>care</u> <u>about,</u> <u>take</u> <u>care</u> <u>of</u>
That carpenter <u>cares</u> <u>for</u> his tools.
Do you <u>care</u> <u>about</u> what happens?
They will <u>take</u> <u>care</u> <u>of</u> him.

depend on

> The property taxes will <u>depend</u> <u>on</u> the new appraisal.

dress in

> Your friend always <u>dresses</u> <u>in</u> white.

explain to

> Did the roofer <u>explain</u> it <u>to</u> you?

operate on

> The staff <u>operated</u> <u>on</u> the patient.

pay for

> What do people usually <u>pay</u> <u>for</u> garbage pickup?

prevent from

> He wants to <u>prevent</u> the roof <u>from</u> leaking.

recover from

> She <u>recovered</u> <u>from</u> the flu rather quickly.

succeed in

> Will they <u>succeed</u> <u>in</u> finding an apartment?

suffer from

> He's <u>suffering</u> <u>from</u> a rare disease.

think of

> They're <u>thinking</u> <u>about</u> adding an extra room to their house.

Exercise S-2: Choose from the two-word verbs above and put them in the correct tense form in the appropriate spaces. Sometimes more than one answer can be appropriate.

1. She was _____ the high prices.

2. They _____ it with cash.

3. My friend _____ asthma when he was a child.

4. I _____ getting here so late. Please excuse me.

5. He _____ getting the loan to pay the bills. He was really happy.

6. Her brother never _____ me about politics.

7. Who _____ her elderly mother when she works?

8. The teacher _____ it _____ the class last week.

9. When did he _____ the job?

10. Someone called and _____ you last night.

Past Perfect and Past Perfect Continuous

A. Past Perfect

I had gone	I had not gone	Had I gone?
You had gone	You had not gone	Had you gone?
We had gone	We had not gone	Had we gone?
They had gone	They had not gone	Had they gone?
He had gone	He had not gone	Had he gone?
She had gone	She had not gone	Had she gone?
It had gone	It had not gone	Had it gone?

Contractions:

had = 'd   had not = hadn't

The past perfect describes an action that happened in the past before another past action: *two actions in the past at different times in one sentence.*

1st past action = past perfect verb; 2nd past action = past verb

The man had vacuumed the living room before his wife returned.

In the above sentence two actions happened at different times in the past. The man first vacuumed, so this is past perfect, and then his wife returned, which is past. The word that connects the two actions is before. Here are some other examples with other connecting words.

The realtor called him after the other people had gone.

They said that they had rented in that neighborhood before.

By the time the plumber arrived, the leaking had stopped.

Exercise S-3: Write in the correct form of the past perfect of the verbs in parentheses.

1. (talk) The contractor _____ with them before he started work.

2. (take) The receptionist _____ her lunch break by the time they got there.

3. (catch) The police reported that they _____ the burglar.

4. (arrive) He telephoned me after they _____.

5. (hear-not) I was sure that I _____ it before.

6. (be) _____ he _____ a good student before he started working?

7. (rent) He asked me why they _____ a furnished apartment.

8. (sign) He _____ already _____ the contract by the time his sister got there.

9. (have) She knew that she _____ never _____ to pay a cleaning fee before.

10. (know)_____they_____ about it before the letter came?

Exercise S-4: Write your own examples of the past perfect using these guide words.

1. _____ before she rented the apartment.
2. The realtor notified me after _____ .
3. The newspaper reported that _____ .
4. By the time we got there, _____ .
5. _____ before _____ .
6. _____ after _____ .
7. _____ said that _____ .
8. By the time _____ , _____ .

Exercise S-5: Answer these questions using the past perfect.

1. What had you done in your native country before you came here?

_____

2. What had you eaten before you came to class?

_____

3. What kind of house had you lived in before you came here?

_____

B. Past Perfect Continuous

I had been taking	I hadn't been taking	Had I been taking?
You had been taking	You hadn't been taking	Had you been taking?
We had been taking	We hadn't been taking	Had we been taking?
They had been taking	They hadn't been taking	Had they been taking?
He had been taking	He hadn't been taking	Had he been taking?
She had been taking	She hadn't been taking	Had she been taking?
It had been taking	It hadn't been taking	Had it been taking?

The past perfect continuous is used the same way as the past perfect, except that the continuous form can mean a longer amount of time.

I had waited an hour before he picked me up.

I had been waiting an hour before he picked me up.

Exercise S-6: Change from the past perfect to the past perfect continuous.

1. He had talked about the complaint before the break ended.

_____

2. By the time the guests showed up, they had waited two hours.

   _____

3. She called me after the tenant had discussed the rent control issue.

   _____

4. You said that you had cleaned the rugs earlier.

   _____

Exercise S-7: Answer these questions using the past perfect continuous.

1. What had you been doing before class started?

   _____

2. What had he been thinking about before he went to the dentist?

   _____

3. What did the TV news report that the leader had been doing?

   _____

4. What had they been discussing by the time the bus came?

   _____

5. What had you been talking about with the manager before the landlady came in?

   _____

6. What had you been doing before you had dinner last night?

   _____

7. Who had you been talking to before you arrived here?

   _____

8. Where had she been living before she moved?

   _____

VI. Composition

Write in the words of your own choice in the spaces using the words in parentheses below each space as guidelines.

Houses in the United States are _____ .
                                        (adjective)

They are usually made of _____ . It's _____ to
                              (materials)   (adjective)

buy a house in this area. The difference between houses here and those in

my native country is that _____
                                 (complete the sentence)

_____ . The best

location for a house to be would be _____
                                            (kind of place)

_____ .

177

Apartments in the United States are _____
(adjective)
and the rents are _____ . To find an
(adjective)
apartment you should _____
(complete the sentence)
_____ . The best kind of landlord is a
person who _____ . The
(complete the sentence)
best thing about living in an apartment is _____
while the worst thing is _____ . The difference
between apartments in my native country and here is _____
_____ .
(complete the sentence)
_____ live(s) in a _____ apartment in
(name of person)   (adjective)
_____ .

    I live in the city of _____ near
(place)
_____ on _____ street. There are many
_____ and few _____ in my neighborhood. My
_____ has _____ rooms
(house/apartment)   (number)
and a _____ . It's a
(extra part: porch, yard, etc.)
_____ place to live. The best thing
(adjective)
about where I live is _____
_____ while the worst thing is _____
_____ .

VII. Pronunciation

A. Vowel

short o (ŏ)

1. r<u>o</u>ck	2. pr<u>o</u>perty	3. dep<u>o</u>sit
<u>o</u>ptional	bl<u>o</u>ck	c<u>o</u>ntract
l<u>o</u>t	cl<u>o</u>set	c<u>a</u>lm

4. The d<u>o</u>ctor l<u>o</u>cked the cl<u>o</u>ck in the cl<u>o</u>set.

5. The c<u>o</u>ntractor rem<u>o</u>deled R<u>o</u>bert's c<u>o</u>ttage.

Contrasts:

short o (ŏ) / short u (ŭ)

6. rob/rub	7. bomb/bum	8. cot/cut
dock/duck	pop/pup	hot/hut
doll/dull	calm/come	shot/shut

178

B. Consonants

J/CH and J/Y

1. joke/choke
   junk/chunk
   jeep/cheap
   badge/batch

2. jam/yam
   juice/use
   jet/yet
   hedge/hay

3. Jane and Jerry cheered the choice of the year.

4. Charles didn't make any jokes about his year in jail.

VIII. Life Skills

A. Classified Ads

501—FURN. APARTMENTS	502—UNFURN. APARTMENTS	513—CONDOMINIUMS
SAN BENITO Furn studio, balcony, close to frwy. $390. 678-5434	SAN BENITO Newly decor., 1-BR, AEK, Nr. trans, no pets, $465 678-0012	MURSTON 3BR, 2BA, pool, sauna, sec., much more, no pets, $950, 678-4442
MURSTON beaut. 2-BR, 1-BA, $655, no pets, 678-0094	SAN BENITO 1-BR, w/den, $600, 688-5678	**522—UNFURN. HOUSE**
MURSTON near hospital, lr. studio, kitch w/dinette, w/w carpets/ drps, enc gar, no pets, $485, 677-6684	**512—UNFURN. DUPLEXES/ TRIPLEXES**	WELLS Spacious + fam. rm., 2 car gar, $950, 678-2212
		WELLS 4-BR, 2½-BA, 2 frplcs, gardener, $1300 mo. 677-4329
DOWNEY brand new 2-BR, 2-BA, washer, dryer, frplcs, refrig., micro, dishwash, $925 secured bldg 645-3331	WELLS Immac 2-BR w/yard, gar. Nr. trans/shops, 1st, last & dep, $500 fee $46, Homefinders, 675-9899	MURSTON 3 BR, 2 BA, large sunny kitchen, gar. inc., Lease/option, Sharon, 679-6676, $1100

Exercise L-1:

1. Mr. Darling is looking for a furnished apartment in San Benito no more than $400. What number should he call?

   _____

2. The number "512" in the classifieds in this paper indicates what kind of housing? _____

   _____

3. Mrs. Tooley has a small dog and is looking for an apartment in this area. Where could she call? _____

4. Tom is looking for an apartment in San Benito. He has furniture and would like to have an extra room for office work. What number should he call? _____

5. What are the extras that come with the condominium advertised here? _____

   _____

6. Identify all the abbreviations in these ads. _____

_____

_____

_____

_____

_____

_____

_____

7. Which place do you have to pay someone for finding it? _____

_____

8. In which house would you not have to worry about taking care of the garden? _____

9. Why do people who write ads often put in the extras such as fireplaces? _____

_____

10. What questions would you ask if you called inquiring about:
    a) the furnished studio in Murston? _____

_____

_____

    b) the unfurnished house in Murston? _____

_____

_____

B. Rental Agreements

There are different kinds of rental agreements, from the very short and simple to the long and complicated. Ask fellow students who rent apartments these questions about their kind of rental agreement.

1. What is the time length of the agreement?
2. What is the rent?
3. How long are you advised before a rent increase?
4. How many people can live in the place?
5. Is the renter allowed to sublet?
6. Are there special rules for the renter?
7. What are the responsibilities of the landlord?
8. What appliances, furniture, etc. are included?
9. Can the landlord or manager enter your apartment?
10. Do all the people living in the apartment have to sign the agreement? Does the landlord sign?
11. Are there damage or cleaning fees?

180

C. Rental Housing Problems

Rental Housing Problems?

If you have a problem with rental housing, such as eviction, 30-day notice to vacate, rent increases, unpaid rent, repairs, damages, deposits, privacy, discrimination or lease and rental agreement questions, contact the Human Relations Division (HRD) of Wilbur County by phoning 346-7867.

This is a non-biased county service available to all tenants and landlords who live in or own property in Wilbur County. We seek to resolve disputes between landlords and tenants by promoting communications and encouraging fair and reasonable renting practices without requiring recourse in the Courts.

Exercise L-2:

1. Who is this county service for?_____
   _____

2. What county service helps out with these rental housing problems?
   _____

3. Choose one of the problems listed and imagine an example of one of them. (For example, with unpaid rent, there is a renter who refuses to pay rent, and yet he won't get out, etc.).

   _____

   _____

   _____

4. What does "non-biased" mean? _____
   _____

5. Why does the county have this service? _____
   _____

D. Utilities Bill

```
┌─────────────────────────────────────────────┬──────────────────┐
│         COUNTY OF JACKSON / WATER BILL        │                  │
│         34 Main St., Jackson, CA 94041        │                  │
│              ───────────                      │                  │
│  Billing Date: 2-20-89                        │  Bob Brown       │
│                                               │  75 Sequoia Ave. │
│  Bi-Monthly Billing for Service at: 75        │  Jackson, CA 94041│
│  Sequoia Ave.                                 │                  │
│  Days of Service: 63   From 12-15-88 to 2-16-89│                 │
└─────────────────────────────────────────────┴──────────────────┘
```

Meter Readings Current Previous	Use in 100 gals	Type of Charge	Amount
4690 4495	195	Water Sewer	21.65 15.60

Account No: 2345594

Previous Balance: Total Due: $37.25

Keep this portion for your records.

Under Resolution 67-79 of the City of Jackson, payment of all charges must be made within 20 days after the date on which billed. If your service is disconnected, the fee for renewal will be $10 during normal working hours and $20 for all other times. Phone 354-3452 8 A.M. to 5 P.M. After 5 P.M. and on Sat., Sun., Holidays, 354-3455.

ACCT. #2345594
Total Due: $37.25

Return
This Portion
With Payment

Exercise L-3:

1. Which section do you send in with your payment? _____
   _____

2. What service time did this cover? _____
   _____

3. Who has to pay this? How much? For exactly what? _____
   _____

4. When is this bill due? _____
   _____

5. What happens if the bill isn't paid? _____
   _____

6. What is the fee for renewal? _____
   _____

7. Who pays your water bill and how much is it usually? _____
   _____

8. What other utility bills do you have? _____
   _____

E. Energy Conservation in the Home

Ways to conserve energy in the home:

1. Install insulation and weatherstrip and caulk windows and doors.
2. Close off unused rooms and shut off their air ducts.
3. Set thermostat between 65-68° daytime in winter, below 65° at night; set at 78° in summer.
4. Close fireplace damper when fireplace is not in use.
5. Clean or replace filters in furnace regularly.
6. In winter keep draperies open in sun, closed at night; in summer, close during day, open at night.
7. Buy the most energy efficient models.
8. Use energy-intensive equipment in early morning or late evening (non-peak time).
9. Turn off radio and TV when not in use.
10. Use dishwasher only with full loads.
11. Wash laundry in warm or cold water, rinse in cold.
12. Take short showers rather than tub baths.
13. Use hand-operated tools, utensils and equipment whenever possible.
14. Concentrate light in reading and work areas.
15. Turn off all lights when not in use.
16. Use florescent lights whenever possible.
17. Repair leaking water faucets with new washers.

Which of the ways listed above do you use to conserve energy? _____

_____

Can you think of other ways to save energy? _____

_____

What do you think of these three people as energy-savers?

a. Mr. and Mrs. Ryan each take hour-long showers every day. They think insulation is a waste of money, and they like a very warm house all the time. They also like to leave all the lights on most of the time because they feel safer. _____

_____

b. Jerry has a lot of electric tools but fixes leaks and uses fluorescent lights. _____

_____

c. Linda is careful about her house's thermostat, the condition of the furnace, and buying energy-efficient models. _____

_____

IX. Problem Solving

Hector, who is from South America, wants to rent an apartment. He went to an apartment that was advertised in the newspaper. When he arrived, he noticed the For Rent sign in the window. When he rang the doorbell, the landlord answered and his smile suddenly turned to a frown. Hector asked about the apartment, the landlord said it was taken, and then slammed the door in his face. Hector started to leave. Then he heard the man inside say, "I don't like those Spanish-speaking people. I'll never rent to them." What should Hector do?

A. What is the problem? _____

_____

_____

_____

B. What are all the possible solutions?_____

_____

_____

_____

C. Which is the best solution?_____

_____

_____

_____

UNIT 9

TRANSPORTATION

The United States is a country on wheels, a true car culture. Anyone who comes here must face the necessity of transportation, whether it be car, bus, train, or plane. This unit will look at using public transportation, getting a driver's license, comprehending or authorizing car repairs, reading signs and obeying the driving laws, all those things that are part of the knowledge so important to moving about in this society.

Objectives

Competencies:
Road Signs
Car Repair
Driver's License
Car Ads
Bus Schedule

Structure:
Conjunctions
Coordinating and Correlatives
Future Perfect Verbs

Pronunciation:
long u ($\overline{u}$)
long u ($\overline{u}$) / long o ($\overline{o}$)
V / F and F / P

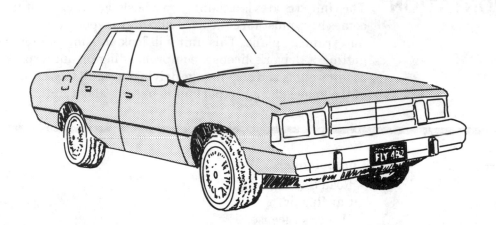

1. identification number
2. windshield
3. wipers
4. hood
5. grill

6. headlights
7. back lights, turning lights, tail lights, brake lights
8. bumper
9. fender

10. license plate
11. tire (spare tire)
12. hubcap
13. trunk
14. door handle
15. side mirror

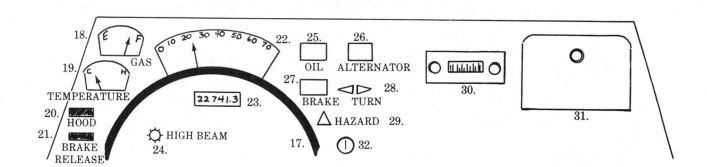

16. dashboard
17. steering wheel
18. gas gauge
19. temperature gauge
20. hood release
21. brake release, hand brake
22. speedometer
23. odometer
24. high beam headlights
25. oil light

26. alternator light
27. brake light
28. turn signal indicator
29. hazard light indicator
30. radio
31. glove compartment
32. ignition key
33. air conditioning
34. rearview mirror
35. sun visor

36. pedals
37. horn
38. automatic transmission
39. clutch
40. gear shift, stick shift
41. engine, motor
42. fuel tank
43. oil stick
44. jack
45. seat belt
46. heater

B. Transportation

1. vehicle
2. taxi (cab)
3. van
4. truck/rig
5. bicycle/bike
6. motorcycle
7. mobile home
8. recreation vehicle
9. bus
10. tram/streetcar
11. train
12. station/depot
13. travel/trip/tour
14. journey
15. itinerary
16. commute/commuter
17. be bound for
18. driver
19. motorist
20. pedestrian
21. road
22. way
23. alley
24. thoroughfare
25. parking lot
26. route
27. pass
28. highway
29. expressway
30. freeway
31. street (St.)
32. avenue (Ave.)
33. drive (Dr.)
34. terrace (Terr.)
35. place (Pl.)
36. cul-de-sac
37. one-way street
38. lane (Ln.)
39. court (Ct.)
40. pavement
41. curb
42. pothole
43. traffic light/signal
44. bump
45. dip
46. intersection/crossing
47. tunnel
48. bridge
49. overpass/underpass
50. boat/ship
51. ferry
52. yacht
53. float
54. sink
55. port
56. harbor
57. pier/dock
58. wharf
59. airplane/plane/aircraft
60. aviation
61. flight
62. take off/depart/ departure
63. land/arrive/arrival
64. schedule
65. delay
66. stopover
67. security
68. baggage claim
69. boarding pass

II. Getting Started

A.

Picture A

1. Describe what's in the picture.
2. Is taking a bus convenient where you live?
3. How is public transportation different in your native country?

Picture B

1. Describe what's in the picture.
2. How often do you drive or ride in a car?
3. What is the difference between transportation by car here and your native country?

Pictures A and B

1. Point out those things that are the same and those things that are different in these pictures.
2. Karen's car broke down and won't be fixed for a week. She doesn't know anyone who can drive her to work or for errands. What should she do?

187

III. Conversation

A.

1. Did you buy a new car recently?
2. No, it's actually a used one. It's only a year old.

1. Was it a good deal?
2. Yes, I got it for a good price and it only has 15,000 miles on it.

1. I usually don't trust used cars. You never know how the previous owner took care of it.
2. I bought this one from a friend of my neighbor. It has a stick shift which I trust more than an automatic transmission.

1. New cars are really expensive. I couldn't afford one with my budget.
2. And they don't get any cheaper.

1. Maybe we should ride horses. It would cut out all those gas, service and pollution expenses.
2. Then we would have to worry about how to pay for what the horse eats!

B.

1. My car broke down on the freeway yesterday.
2. What did you do, fix it yourself?

1. I have insurance so I just called to have it towed to a gas station.
2. That does help out, especially on the freeway where cars go so fast. What did the problem turn out to be?

1. The mechanic said it was some kind of electrical short. They ended up putting in a new battery.
2. Did it take a long time? Once I had to wait two days because they didn't have the right part.

1. I waited only an hour at the gas station but the whole thing took most of the afternoon. It was a lousy way to spend my day off.
2. You can say that again.

C.

1. How do you usually get around?
2. I don't have the money for a car yet, so I have to either walk or use the bus a lot.

1. How is the bus service here?
2. It's not bad. You can get about quite easily and it won't burn a hole in your pocket.

1. My old car isn't very economical. It wastes gas and it seems to spend more time in the repair shop than on the road.
2. Sounds like a real lemon. It would be nice if we could walk or bike everywhere.
1. That would be ideal. It's too bad that we live so far away from everything.
2. Well, the world gets smaller and yet in another way it gets bigger. I hope there will be more convenient public transportation in the future.

Dialogue Puzzle: With a partner fill in the appropriate responses or questions in the spaces of the dialogue below, then practice and read to the rest of the class.

1. Why did you go to the airport last night?
2. _____

1. Was the flight on time?
2. _____

1. _____
2. It's always crowded on Friday nights.

1. _____
2. No, we got our baggage right away.

1. I hate it when the plane gets delayed.
2. _____

1. Security seems to be a growing problem too.
2. _____

Discussion: Answer the following questions about things talked about in the previous conversations.

1. What was the best trip you have ever taken?
2. Did you ever have car trouble?
3. Did you or a friend ever have a car accident?
4. Where is the best place to drive a car?
5. Why do people in the USA generally prefer cars over public transportation?

IV. Reading

A. Vocabulary

drive off	went dead	lemon	mechanic
intersection	turn over	have a look	upcoming
on our way	stuck	worth a try	task
ignition	dejectedly	hood	blew his top

B. Reading

Sabine finished class at the adult school and headed for the bus stop. As she was walking along the sidewalk, a car pulled up by the curb and a voice came out, "Do you want a ride home?" Sabine looked inside the car and saw her classmates, Michiyo from Japan and Mohammed from Afghanistan. "Sure," she said, "if you don't mind. I live on the other side of town near the county park."

"It's on our way," Michiko responded, "because I'm taking Mohammed to the dentist near there."

Sabine got in and they drove off until the first intersection where the car stopped and the engine went dead. Michiyo tried the ignition but it wouldn't turn over. "Oh, no, we're stuck," she said dejectedly to the others. "Could you push the car to the other side of the road and to that gas station up ahead?"

They pushed the car through the light traffic to the front of the gas station where Mohammed offered to have a look under the hood first. "Do you know a lot about cars?" Sabine asked.

Mohammed shrugged his shoulders and said, "Very little but it's worth a try." He then proceeded to push and pull several wires and loosen and tighten other things, but in the end the car still didn't work. Michiyo went over to the mechanic in the gas station and explained the problem to him.

Sabine and Mohammed said goodbye to Michiyo and began to walk to the bus stop. They talked about their upcoming class party. Michiyo called her son's nursery school and explained that she would be late. Then she had the hard task of calling her husband to tell him that the car had another problem. He always blew his top when he heard bad news about their car which he thought was a real lemon.

C. Exercises

1. Write these sentences in the correct time sequence, using a 1 for what happened first all the way to 7 as last.

   _____ a. Michiyo talked to the mechanic about her car.

   _____ b. Michiyo's car stalled at the intersection.

   _____ c. Sabine and Mohammed pushed the car.

   _____ d. Sabine walked out of class toward the bus stop.

   _____ e. Sabine and Mohammed walked to the bus stop.

_____ f. Sabine asked Mohammed if he knew a lot about cars.

_____ g. Michiyo offered Sabine a ride home.

2. Write *true* or *false*.

_____ a. Sabine was studying at the adult school.

_____ b. Mohammed was planning on going to the bank.

_____ c. Michiyo's car broke down on the freeway.

_____ d. The street where they stopped was very crowded.

_____ e. Mohammed knew only a little about cars.

_____ f. Sabine and Mohammed talked about future festivities.

_____ g. Michiyo's husband didn't really like their car.

3. Vocabulary: Put the vocabulary words from Section A (page 190) in the spaces.

   a. The machine just suddenly _____ and I had to call someone to fix it.

   b. The garage _____ said, "Oh, it's _____ _____."

   c. When the engine wouldn't _____ , he got angry and _____ and walked back home.

   d. He'll _____ at the calendar and then tell you what are the _____ events at the concert hall.

   e. The student was _____ on number 13 of the exam; she couldn't figure it out.

   f. Why did they _____ in their car so quickly without saying goodbye?

   g. _____ back home we had to stop at the red light of every _____ .

   h. It's a problem with the _____ of the car. It just won't start.

   i. He's going to look under the _____ to check everything out.

   j. The boy talked _____ about his father's death.

   k. That car is a real _____ . It spends more time in the garage than on the road.

191

II. Structure

| Coordinating and Correlative Conjunctions |

A conjunction is a word that connects words, phrases or clauses. The most popular conjunctions are and, or and but, which are used below.

Words: the wipers and the windshield

Phrases: at night or in the evening

Clauses (groups of words with a subject and verb, like a sentence):
   I need a map but I can't find one.

A. A coordinating conjunction joins words or groups of words that are of the same order. The main conjunctions of this type are those used above: and, but and or.

The train and the car accidents happened in the same part of the city.

He opened the glove compartment but it was empty.

You can drive to the next town or get gas here.

Exercise S-1: Write in the correct coordinating conjunction.

1. He turned the ignition key _____ the car wouldn't start.

2. He's taking a plane _____ a boat on the trip.

3. A bus _____ a train will get you there. You can choose which one is more convenient.

Exercise: Write your own sentences with these conjunctions.

1. _____

2. _____

3. _____

B. Correlative conjunctions are used in pairs or series to connect words, phrases or clauses. The main correlative conjunctions are:

as . . . as	not only . . . but (also)
so . . . as (negative)	so . . . that
both . . . and	such . . . that
either . . . or	whether . . . or (for doubt or
neither . . . nor	uncertainty)

She's as tired as you are.

The problem with your car isn't so serious as I first thought it was.

The safety officer talked about both car care and accident prevention.

Either Bob or Nick will bring the car parts.

He prefers neither a sports car nor a van.

192

They <u>not only</u> had a bike <u>but also</u> a motorcycle.

He became <u>so</u> tired <u>that</u> he finally had to quit.

It was <u>such</u> a problem <u>that</u> they had to ask for special help.

I'm <u>not sure whether</u> they'll come <u>or</u> not.

Exercise S-2: Write in appropriate correlative conjunctions in the spaces.

1. She likes _____ art _____ music. She paints beautiful pictures and plays the piano.

2. The storm _____ destroyed the tunnel _____ the bridge. There was a lot of damage.

3. He isn't _____ smart _____ his sister.

4. She isn't sure _____ she'll go _____ not.

5. You can take _____ the cake _____ the fruit, but choose just one.

6. The film was _____ bad _____ we left.

7. He's _____ nice _____ you.

8. It's _____ a mess _____ you can't even find the phone.

9. He hates sports. He plays _____ tennis _____ basketball.

Exercise: Now write your own examples of the correlative conjunctions in the spaces below.

1. _____

2. _____

3. _____

4. _____

5. _____

6. _____

7. _____

8. _____

9. _____

Future Perfect Verb

I will have spoken	I will not have spoken	Will I have spoken?
You will have spoken	You will not have spoken	Will you have spoken?
We will have spoken	We will not have spoken	Will we have spoken?
They will have spoken	They will not have spoken	Will they have spoken?
He will have spoken	He will not have spoken	Will he have spoken?
She will have spoken	She will not have spoken	Will she have spoken?
It will have spoken	It will not have spoken	Will it have spoken?

The future perfect tense is used for an action that has already happened at a certain moment in the future. For example, my friend went on a trip and now I want to visit him at his home. I want to make sure that he will arrive before I go there. I ask his mother and she says, "He will have returned by next Monday when you wish to visit."

We will have finished fixing your car by the time you get off work.

Will the package have gotten there by next Sunday?

Exercise S-3: Write in the correct form of the future perfect.

1. (finish) He is certain that they _____ the project by next year.

2. (change) By this afternoon he _____ all the tires.

3. (clean) They will be here at two o'clock and he _____ the car by then.

4. (take) She says she _____ all the pictures of the wreck before the tow truck will come.

5. (set) By the time she comes I _____ already _____ the itinerary for the trip.

6. (not-forget) You _____ the things I told you when you reach my age.

7. (be) _____ you _____ in the United States two years by Christmas?

8. (become) Hopefully, in another fifty years nuclear weapons _____ obsolete.

9. (understand) Perhaps he _____ that all men are created equal by the time he grows up.

10. (fly) The pilot _____ over five hundred hours without an accident by next August.

Exercise S-4: Answer these questions with a complete sentence using the future perfect.

1. What will you have finished doing by next year? _____

   _____

2. What will you have accomplished by this evening? _____

   _____

3. Who will you have talked to by four o'clock? _____

   _____

4. What will have happened in the world in ten years? _____

   _____

5. How many books will you have finished reading by the end of the year?

   _____

6. Where will you have already visited by the first of the month?

   _____

VI. Composition

Write in the words of your own choice in the spaces using the words in parentheses below each space as guidelines.

I have traveled by many kinds of transportation, including

_____ , _____ and _____ . Of these
(3 kinds of transportation)

three I prefer _____ the most because _____
(transportation)

_____ . I came to
(complete the sentence)

this country by _____ . The trip took me
(transportation)

_____ . I arrived at _____ quite
(how long)

_____ . I was _____ that _____
(adjective)   (adjective)   (person/no one)

met me.

In my native country, the most popular kind of transportation is

_____ . I used to get around by _____ .
(transportation)   (transportation)

The roads there are _____ and the
(adjective)

bridges are _____ . Public transportation

is _____ . The type of car that many people

like to buy is _____ . Traffic on the roads is
(kind of car)

_____ . Drivers generally drive _____ .
(how)

The difference between the United States and my native country in

transportation use is _____

_____ . In the future people will probably use

_____ . The problem of _____
(future transportation)   (future transportation problem)

_____ will have been worked on and resolved by then.

VII. Pronunciation

A. Vowel

long u ($\bar{u}$)

1. r<u>oo</u>m
   comm<u>u</u>te
   wh<u>o</u>se

2. thr<u>ou</u>gh
   r<u>ou</u>te
   fl<u>ew</u>

3. aven<u>ue</u>
   rearv<u>iew</u>
   s<u>oo</u>n

4. L<u>ou</u>is had t<u>wo</u> r<u>ou</u>tes in J<u>u</u>ne.

5. The gr<u>ou</u>p from the sch<u>oo</u>l fl<u>ew</u> at n<u>oo</u>n.

Contrast: long u ($\bar{u}$) / long o ($\bar{o}$)

6. to/toe	7. whose/hose	8. do/dough
through/throw	shoe/show	moon/moan
blew/blow	soon/sewn	June/Joan

B. Consonant

V / F and F / P

1. veil/fail
   van/fan
   reviews/refuse
   save/safe

2. fair/pair
   fool/pool
   suffer/supper
   chief/cheap

3. Few people refused to believe that the ferry was safe.

4. The police chief praised the first prize winner.

VIII. Life Skills   A. Road Signs

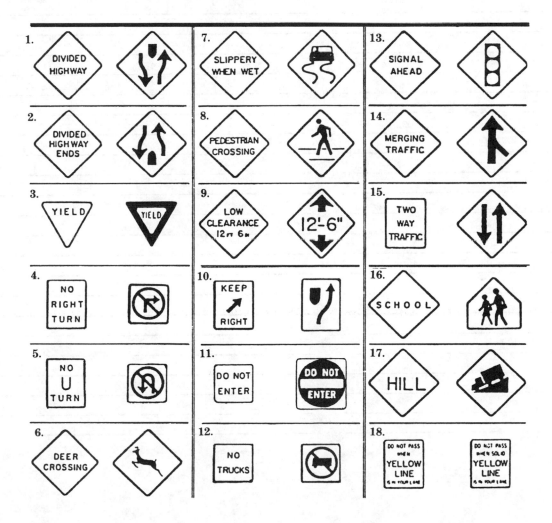

Exercise L-1: Study the road signs on page 197. Then complete the exercise below.

Sign	Where do you see it?	What does it mean?
1.		
2.		
3.		
4.		
5.		
6.		
7.		
8.		
9.		
10.		
11.		
12.		
13.		
14.		
15.		
16.		
17.		
18.		

B. Car Repair

Shaff's Auto Service Center
34 Osgood Dr.   Phone 299-5513
Carson City, Nevada

Name Karen Lee
Address 9 Ray Drive C.C.
Phone 296-0130
Date 5-15-86

All Work Guaranteed on Foreign & American Cars and Trucks

MAKE	MODEL	YEAR	LICENSE	MILEAGE	TERMS	TIME PROMISED
Ford	Granada	82	587 CAL	30,789	Check	4:30 P.M.

Parts Necessary and Estimate of Labor Required	Est. Parts Cost	Est. Labor Cost
Inspect noise at left front when brakes are applied.		
Remove and put back brake drums.		30.00
Revised estimate OK by phone 11 AM		
Parts for brake job	32.85	
Labor		60.00
Totals	32.85	60.00
GRAND TOTAL	$92.85	

I hereby authorize the above repair work to be done along with necessary materials. It is understood that this company assumes no responsibility for loss or damage by theft or fire to vehicles placed with them for storage, sale, repair or while testing.

Signed:_____

Exercise L-2:

1. Why did the customer bring the car to the garage? _____
_____

2. How much was the original estimate and what was it for? ____
_____

3. Who is the customer? What kind of car does she have? When is she supposed to pick up the car? _____
_____

4. Did the customer give permission for the revised estimate? How?
_____

5. How much is the final estimate for parts? Labor? Total? _____
_____

6. Was the customer treated fairly? _____
_____

Could you imagine a situation where it wouldn't be fair?_____
_____

199

C. Driver's License

Information questions asked when applying for a driver's license.

---

1. Do you have a visual, physical or mental condition that impairs your ability to drive? If so, explain _____

   _____

2. Have you been convicted within the past ten years in this state or elsewhere of any offense resulting from your operation of or involving a motor vehicle? _____

   _____

3. Has your license or privilege to drive been suspended or revoked in this state or elsewhere? _____
   If the answer to questions 2 or 3 is "yes," show court, date and kind of offense(s). List each separately _____

   _____

4. Show in space provided any valid out of state license held by you.

   State _____ License No. _____

Exercise L-3:

1. Jim lost his right arm in an accident. Would he indicate this here? If so, where. _____

   _____

2. Marcia was arrested and convicted of drunk driving three years ago, March 3rd, at Olympia Court House. What should she write for #2 and #3? (Her license was suspended for 90 days at that time.)

   _____

   _____

3. Gary lived in Virginia and had a driver's license. Then he moved to New York. What should he write in the spaces in #4? (License number in Virginia was 342 JHL.) _____

   _____

D. Car Ads

Honest John's Used Cars
OPEN 7 DAYS: 9 A.M.—9 P.M.

'79 HONDA CVCC, auto	$ 2995
'81 FORD FAIRMONT, auto, ps, pb, air, am/fm stereo	$ 3995
'82 NISSAN SENTRA, 4-door, ps, pb, am/fm	$ 4795
'73 BUICK WAGON, full power, 9 passenger	$ 795
'85 MAZDA GLC, 4-speed, loaded	$ 5995

Exercise L-4:

1. Explain the abbreviations in the ad above. _____

_____

_____

2. Choose one of the cars above and ask questions about it as if you were interested in buying it. _____

_____

_____

3. Bring an example of a new car ad and a used car ad from the newspaper or a magazine and compare the differences. _____

_____

_____

E. Bus Schedule

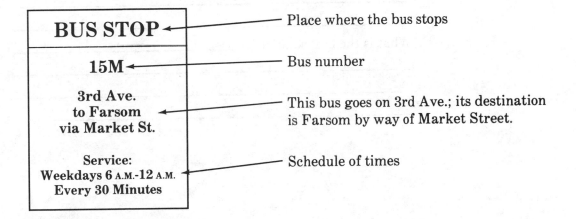

BUS STOP	← Place where the bus stops
15M ←	Bus number
3rd Ave. to Farsom via Market St. ←	This bus goes on 3rd Ave.; its destination is Farsom by way of Market Street.
Service: Weekdays 6 A.M.-12 A.M. Every 30 Minutes ←	Schedule of times

Exercise L-5:

BUS STOP

43C

Hillsdale to Elm via Galant Blvd.

Service:
24 hr. Weekdays
Every 15 min.
No service
Sat./Sun./Hol.

1. What bus stops here? _____
2. Where does the bus route end? _____
3. I want to go to Elm but my friend wants to get off on Galant Blvd. Is this possible? _____
4. Can you catch a bus on this route at 2 A.M. Sunday? 3 A.M. Tuesday?

_____

5. How often do buses run on this route? _____
6. How often do buses run in your city? _____

_____

IX. Problem Solving

Mr. and Mrs. Tron have a teenage son who just turned 16. He loves cars and wants to drive very badly to impress his friends. He passed his driver's test after failing it four times. He likes to drive fast. Mrs. Tron is afraid that he will get in a big accident if he gets his own car. The boy is working at a fast food restaurant to save up enough money to buy a used car. Mr. Tron doesn't care about it. "It's his money," he says. "Let him do whatever he wants with it." Mrs. Tron begins to cry and says, "If he just took the bus for a few more years, I would feel better. He's just too young now to have his own car."

A. What is the problem? _____

_____

_____

_____

B. What are all the possible solutions?_____

_____

_____

_____

C. What is the best solution? _____

_____

_____

_____

UNIT 10

EDUCATION

Education is important for us because it represents our future. One thing that probably holds true for everyone is the high value placed on education in countries throughout the world. Education begins when we are very young and continues throughout life in one way or another. This unit will take us to that region where we are always learning.

Objectives

Competencies:

Adult School Registration
Educational Profile Form
School Absence Excuse
Directions for an Exam

Structure:

Conjunctions
Subordinating of Time, Condition, Reason, Result and Comparison

Pronunciation:

U
U / long u ($\bar{u}$), U (aw)
D / B and H / WH

I. Vocabulary

A. People

1. teacher/instructor/ professor
2. faculty
3. staff
4. teacher's aide
5. substitute
6. principal/director
7. superintendent
8. board of education
9. counselor
10. PTA (Parent Teacher Association)
11. special ed teacher
12. tutor
13. student council

B. School

1. registration
2. admission requirements
3. class schedule
4. attendance
5. tuition
6. textbook
7. subject/class/course
8. curriculum
9. term/semester/session/ quarter
10. test/exam/quiz
11. literate/illiterate
12. certificate/diploma/ degree
13. promote
14. grade/report card
15. grade point average
16. scholarship
17. transfer
18. drop out
19. suspension/expulsion
20. parent-teacher conference
21. coeducational (coed)
22. private/public school
23. student loan

C. Subjects

1. mathematics
2. algebra
3. geometry
4. grammar
5. literature
6. handwriting
7. geography
8. social studies
9. physical education
10. art
11. history
12. spelling
13. science
14. music
15. speech
16. biology
17. sociology
18. anthropology
19. psychology
20. archeology
21. geology
22. chemistry
23. physics
24. engineering
25. medicine
26. law
27. education
28. philosophy
29. computer science
30. political science
31. economics

D. Education in the United States

Ages	Type of School	Grades	Subjects
2-5	preschool, nursery school		Early educational skills
6	kindergarten		Introduction to schooling
	elementary school grammar school grade school	1-5 (6 or 8)	Fundamentals of reading and and mathematics, social studies, science, spelling, English, art and PE (physical education)
	junior high school middle school	(6)-7-8-(9)	More advanced studies at all levels

	high school
	  freshman, sophomore,
	  junior, senior
		(9)-10-11-12	More advanced studies, preparation for college or jobs

School attendance required through 16 years of age.

junior college community college	13-14		Opportunities for degrees or entrance to a university

university/college
  undergraduate
	13-16		Choice of career study
			  BA = Bachelor of Arts degree
			    for liberal arts students
			  BS = Bachelor of Science degree
			    for science students

graduate/postgraduate
  MA = Master of Arts
  MS = Master of Science
  MEd = Master of Education

MBA = Master of Business Arts
PhD = Doctor of Philosophy
MD = Doctor of Medicine

Other kinds of schools:
  Vocational School
  Adult School
  Law School
  Community Education

Continuation High School
School of Cosmetology
Business College

List the levels of schools in your native country, following the pattern of section D.

_____   _____
_____   _____
_____   _____
_____   _____
_____   _____

II. Getting Started

A.

B.

Picture A

1. Describe what's in the picture.
2. What do children learn in a school like this one?
3. How are schools like this one compared to those in your native country?

Picture B

1. Describe what's in the picture.
2. What do students learn in a school like this one?
3. How are schools like this one compared to those in your native country?

Pictures A and B

1. Point out those things that are similar and those things that are different in these pictures
2. Harry wants to go to college and become an engineer. Now he works as a waiter in a restaurant. He's single and has a small savings account. What should he do?

III. Conversation

A.

1. I came here a little over three years ago.
2. Really? What brought you here?

1. I didn't have much of a choice. I was a war refugee.
2. Did you have difficulties in adjusting to this culture?

1. Actually quite a few. My family had everything and then suddenly we had nothing.
2. It must have been hard trying to start your life over again, especially in a culture like this one.

1. Everyone has treated us very nicely.
2. That's good to hear.

1. The hardest thing is to start my education all over again.
2. Do you have a degree?

1. Yes, but it won't help me find a job here. I have to go back to school.
2. Well, I wish you the best of luck.

B.

1. Yesterday my cousin graduated from high school.
2. His diploma will be useful for getting a job.

1. Now he wants to go to college.
2. What's he planning on studying?

1. Electronics.
2. Does he have any future jobs lined up?

1. Not right now, but he's interested in the big electronics industry in the Santa Clara Valley.
2. Yes, I heard that it is really booming.

1. I just hope he can get through all his studies with flying colors.
2. It takes a lot of hard work, but it's worth it.

C.

1. This English is too difficult! I'll never learn it.
2. Don't get yourself down. You're improving every day.

1. But why does it take so long? I feel like I'm going nowhere. Maybe I'm too old to learn.
2. Oh, you're never too old to learn. Education is a lifetime experience.

1. I guess you're right.
2. You are not only learning English but you're also taking care of a lot of other responsibilities.

1. Which reminds me, I have to pick up my kids at school.
2. You'd better get going. See you later.

1. Thanks for the encouragement.
2. Keep studying now.

Dialogue Puzzle: With a partner fill in the appropriate responses or questions in the spaces of the dialogue below, then practice and read to the rest of the class.

1. What was your favorite subject in school?
2. _____

1. Did you get good grades in it?
2. _____

1. _____
2. _____ was the most difficult for me.

1. _____
2. Because _____ .

1. Who was your favorite teacher?
2. _____

1. What did you like about him/her?
2. _____

IV. Reading

A. Vocabulary

community	remind	conference	find the time
support	honor	grade	get out of
reluctantly	attend	scholarship	a taste of his own
veterinarian	homework		medicine

B. Reading

Giovanni Gotelli always had a problem with his children about watching TV instead of doing their homework. Sandra was a sophomore at the nearby high school, and Mario was a 5th grader in the elementary school. "Turn off that dumb box," he would yell at them. "Study. I never had the chance to get a good education because I had to work to support my family when I was young."

Sandra and Mario were tired of hearing this same speech so many times. They both had good grades at school and were even on the principal's honor list. Sandra wanted to get a scholarship to a university and study to become a veterinarian. Mario just enjoyed playing soccer in PE class. He and his father were big soccer fans.

One morning as the whole Gotelli family was getting ready for school and work, Sandra reminded her mother and father about the parent-teacher conference and open house at her school in the evening. Giovanni suddenly remembered that there was an important soccer game on TV at that time.

When he tried to get out of going to the conference, his wife said, "You're not going to watch that dumb box! You always give this speech to your kids, so here's a taste of your own medicine. Education is more important than a soccer game. We're going to our daughter's school!" She grabbed his coat and gave it to him. Giovanni reluctantly agreed. They all laughed, especially his kids, as they went off to school.

C. Exercises

1. Write these sentences in the correct time sequence of the story, using a 1 for what came first all the way to 7 as last.

_____ a. Sandra informed her parents about the school activity.

_____ b. The Gotelli family immigrated to the United States.

_____ c. Giovanni remembered the game on TV.

_____ d. Giovanni's wife scolded him.

_____ e. Sandra and Mario registered in the American schools.

_____ f. Giovanni said he would attend the school function.

_____ g. Mario and Sandra laughed at their dad.

2. Write *true* or *false*.

_____ a. It bothered Giovanni that his kids watched TV instead of doing their homework.

_____ b. Giovanni's youth was the same as his kids'.

_____ c. Mario was not yet in high school.

_____ d. Giovanni was a soccer fan.

_____ e. Mario and Sandra were good students.

_____ f. Sandra wanted to eventually work with animals.

_____ g. Giovanni thought TV was a great educational tool.

3. Vocabulary: Put the vocabulary words from Section A (page 208) in the appropriate blank spaces.

a. Each of the _____ students will probably get a _____ to a university.

b. He _____ did his math _____ after dinner. He hated doing it.

c. When will I ever _____ to get this work done? I'm so busy.

d. There is a lot of parent _____ for the children's soccer leagues in this suburban _____ .

e. The _____ carefully checked the horse's leg.

f. What did you _____ or learn from that program on apartheid?

g. Please _____ me to _____ the next health _____ in the state. It's a good chance to meet interesting people and learn new things.

h. My brother got a good _____ in history.

i. The selfish man got _____ when no one would lend him money when he needed it.

209

V. Structure

A clause is a group of words with a subject and a verb. A main clause can be by itself, that is, independent.

Mary called me last night.

A subordinating or dependent clause cannot be by itself; it needs other words to make its meaning clear and complete.

. . . after she talked with her parents.

This subordinate clause needs a main clause to make its meaning clear and complete. We are asking, "What happened after she talked with her parents?"

Mary called me last night after she talked with her parents.

The word after in the above sentence is a subordinating conjunction, and it connects the main clause with the subordinating clause. The most commonly used subordinating conjunctions are listed in the following categories: time, condition, reason, result and comparison.

A. Time: after, before, when, while, until (till), as

Examples:

He asked about the admission requirements <u>after</u> he had picked up the class schedule.

<u>Before</u> they raised the tuition, they held a public meeting.

I'll ask about the length of the term <u>when</u> I get there.

<u>While</u> Sara was studying, her husband prepared dinner.

He won't get a scholarship <u>until</u> he studies harder.

He dropped out of school <u>as</u> I was getting ready to graduate.

Exercise: Write examples of your own using these kinds of conjunctions.

1. (after)_____

2. (before) _____

3. (when) _____

4. (while) _____

5. (until)_____

6. (as) _____

B. Condition: although, though, if, unless

Examples:

<u>Although</u> his major isn't math, he still knows a lot about it.

<u>Though</u> geometry is hard, it's still interesting.

<u>If</u> you show me his report card, the tutor can help.

I won't go <u>unless</u> it's free.

Exercise: Write examples of your own using these kinds of conjunctions.

    1. (although) _____

    2. (though) _____

    3. (if) _____

    4. (unless) _____

C. Reason: because, since

Examples:

My friend called <u>because</u> he needed to find out the homework.

<u>Since</u> it's so late, I'll say goodbye now and talk to you tomorrow.

Exercise: Write your own examples using these conjunctions.

    1. (because) _____

    2. (since) _____

D. Result: in order that, so that

Examples:

I explained everything very slowly <u>in order that</u> he would completely understand the document.

She studied hard <u>so that</u> she could go to college.

Exercise: Write your own examples using these conjunctions.

    1. (in order that) _____

    2. (so that) _____

E. Comparison: than

Example:

He writes faster <u>than</u> he types.

Exercise: Write an example using this kind of conjunction.

    1. (than) _____

Exercise S-1: Choose the correct subordinating conjuctions for the spaces below.

1. _____ he's tired, he'll help you.
2. They called the district _____ they wanted the nearest elementary school in the area.
3. He won't come _____ you invite him.
4. They write neater _____ they keep their rooms.
5. He gave them a map _____ they wouldn't get lost.
6. _____ he was studying science, the boy interrupted him.
7. _____ they offer courses in music, I'll let you know.
8. She had set the table _____ she started cooking.
9. I'll give you a ride _____ you'll get there on time.
10. She won't call _____ she gets settled in her new school.

Exercise: Finish these sentences with appropriate clauses.

1. When you want to find out about a high school, _____
   _____ .

2. Although it's difficult, _____
   _____ .

3. _____
   _____ before the program started.

4. She called the school because _____
   _____ .

5. _____
   unless you fill out an application form.

6. He talks more slowly than he _____
   _____ .

7. _____ in order that he would get good grades.

8. _____ until everything is finished.

9. Since it's a holiday, _____ .

10. He did his science project while _____
    _____ .

212

Conditional Sentences

A conditional sentence has two clauses, a dependent clause that begins with <u>if</u> and a main clause.

Examples:

If he studies for two hours, his mother will be happy.
   (dependent clause)   (main clause)

I won't come if the teacher isn't there.
  (main)   (dependent)

There are three kinds of conditional sentences:

A. Future/Possible

This describes an action that can happen in the future. The dependent clause is in the present tense and the main clause is in the future.

Example:

If she <u>has</u> enough credits, she<u>'ll</u> <u>transfer</u> to the university.
    (present)   (future)

Exercise S-2: Write the correct form of the verb in these sentences.

1. (meet) If you don't call, I _____ you at school.

2. (give) If Ramon _____ me the information for the exam, I'll pass it on to you.

3. (show up) They_____ if you tell them in advance.

4. (have) I will blow my top if we _____ more homework.

5. (not speak) If the teacher _____ more slowly, I'll never understand.

Exercise: Finish these sentences with your own clauses.

1. If he gets a suspension from school, _____
   _____ .

2. _____ if they don't have time.

3. If I study computer science, _____
   _____ .

4. _____
   I'll complain about it.

5. Your friends will help you _____
   _____ .

213

In this kind of conditional sentence, the main clause can also use the helping verbs <u>may, can, should</u> or <u>must</u> instead of will, depending on the intended meaning.

Examples:

If you <u>give</u> me her number, I <u>can notify</u> her.

They <u>may come</u> if you <u>invite</u> them.

If you <u>make</u> a mistake on the form, you <u>should start</u> again.

The kids <u>must behave</u> if they <u>stay.</u>

Exercise: Finish these sentences with your own clauses.

1. I can tell you about it in more detail if _____
   _____ .

2. If _____
   they may leave.

3. The student should notify the teacher if _____
   _____ .

4. If _____ he must
   obey all the rules.

B. Present/Not Now

In this kind of conditional sentence there is a wish for something to happen but it hasn't happened yet. The dependent clause is in the past tense and the main clause uses <u>would, should, could</u> or <u>might</u>.

Example:

If he <u>went</u> to school, he <u>would learn.</u>
    (past)   (would + present verb)

Notice that in the above sentence that there is a wish that he would learn but for now he doesn't go to school.

Exercise S-3: Write in the correct form of the verb.

1. (be) If her children got better grades, she _____
   happier.

2. (speak) He _____ to more people if he
   knew English better.

3. (know) If Betty _____ why it happened, she
   could tell you.

4. (not buy) Mrs. Meyer _____ the sodas if
   they had artificial flavoring.

5. (have) I might quit that job if I _____ an
   unfair boss.

214

Exercise: Complete these conditional sentences with your own clauses.

1. If I knew the office hours, _____ .
2. _____ if they took the exam.
3. The big country would send military arms to the small country _____ .
4. If the student failed the exam _____ .
5. _____ if she had the time.

Dependent clauses in this type of conditional sentence use the past tense with all verbs except to be. To be uses were with all persons in clauses, including I, she, he and it. (I were, you were, we were, they were, he were, she were, it were)

Exercise: Finish these sentences with your own clauses.

1. If I were richer, _____ .
2. _____ if she were older.
3. If I were you, _____ .

C. Past/Not then

In this kind of conditional sentence there is a wish for something to have happened in the past, but it didn't happen. The dependent clause is in the past perfect tense and the main clause uses would have, should have, might have or could have plus the past participle.

If you had given me the money, I would have bought it.

    (past perfect)   (would have + past participle)

Notice in the above example that there is a wish for something to have happened in the past (to give the money) but it didn't happen. ("I" didn't buy it.)

Exercise S-4: Write in the correct form of the verb.

1. (give) If he had told me, I _____ it to him.
2. (be) If the weather _____ bad, they could had stayed home.
3. (get) His mother might have bought him a toy if he _____ _____ a good grade on his spelling test.
4. (notify) If you _____ the teacher sooner, he might have let you turn in the report next week.
5. (do) I would have been pleased if they _____ _____ their homework.

215

Exercise: Complete the sentences.

1. He could have gone to college if _____

_____ .

2. _____ if the doctor

had not operated.

3. The leaders could have avoided a war _____

_____ .

4. _____ we might have

found the school easier.

5. If the program had been shorter _____

_____ .

Exercise S-5: Write in the correct form of the verb in parentheses using the rules for all three kinds of conditional sentences.

1. (come) He _____ if he had the time.
2. (meet) The PTA _____ in the
library if it is free.
3. (not visit) They _____
her if they had known about her problems.
4. (not have) Pierre can't write if _____ a pen.
5. (tell) I couldn't have known if nobody _____ me.
6. (try) She would get a job if she _____ harder.

Exercise: Complete the following conditional sentences.

1. If I were rich _____ .
2. If they were enjoying studying science, _____

_____ .

3. The students would have done their homework if _____

_____ .

4. They will come to your house if _____

_____ .

5. If I were in my native country _____

_____ .

6. Many will die of starvation if _____

_____ .

7. If they called before eight _____ .
8. I would have called you last night if _____

_____ .

VI. Composition

Write in the words of your own choice in the spaces using the words in parentheses below each space as guidelines.

Education in the United States is _____ . It seems that the best thing about schools here is _____ _____ while the worst thing is _____ . In my native country education is _____ . Teaching there is a _____ career. The difference between schools here and there is _____ _____ .

When I was young in school, my favorite subject was _____ and the teacher that I remember the most was _____ who taught _____ . The subject that I hated was _____ because _____ _____ . When I got older, my favorite class was _____ . I liked it because _____ _____ . One thing that I learned in school that helped me later in life was _____ _____ .

I think that education is _____ for society. Educated people usually _____ . Parents
(what do they do)
should always _____ .
(what to do for children who are students)

217

VII. Pronunciation

A. Vowel

(U)

1. c<u>oul</u>d	2. f<u>oo</u>t	3. f<u>u</u>ll
b<u>oo</u>k	s<u>u</u>gar	w<u>o</u>man
sh<u>oul</u>d	p<u>u</u>sh	w<u>oo</u>d

4. The c<u>oo</u>k sh<u>oul</u>d p<u>u</u>ll the h<u>oo</u>d.

5. He p<u>u</u>t the textb<u>oo</u>k on the c<u>u</u>shion.

Contrast:

U / long u (ū) and U / (aw)

6. pull/pool	7. wool/wall	8. full/fall
full/fool	took/talk	foot/fought
should/shoe	hook/hawk	cushion/caution

B. Consonants

D / B and H / Wh

1. <u>d</u>are/<u>b</u>are	2. <u>h</u>eat/<u>wh</u>eat
<u>d</u>ig/<u>b</u>ig	<u>h</u>en/<u>wh</u>en
pe<u>d</u>al/pe<u>bb</u>le	<u>h</u>eal/<u>wh</u>eel
roa<u>d</u>/ro<u>b</u>e	<u>h</u>air/<u>wh</u>ere

3. <u>H</u>enry <u>w</u>ondered <u>wh</u>ere his <u>w</u>ife's ro<u>b</u>e <u>w</u>as.

4. <u>B</u>arbara gra<u>bb</u>ed the pe<u>bb</u>le near the <u>d</u>rain.

VIII. Life Skills

A. Registration and Student Profile

Fill in the registration and profile for yourself.

PLAINVILLE ADULT SCHOOL

Please Print   Date_____

Name: _____
                          (last)   (first)   (middle)

Address:_____City:_____Zip:_____

Phone: (home) _____ (work) _____ Sex: Male _____ Female _____

Birthdate: _____ County of Birth:_____

In an Emergency, call:_____Phone:_____

Educational Background and Professional Goals

A. Circle the number of years of education you completed in your country:

      1 2 3 4 5 6 7 8 9 10 11 12 / University or College 1 2 3 4 5+

B. Do you have a high school diploma or certificate? Yes _____ No _____

C. Did you study English before? Yes _____ No _____ If "Yes," how long did you study in your native country? _____In the U.S.?_____

D. If you went to a university, what was your major study? _____

E. What are your reasons for learning English?

    _____ to help in day-to-day living

    _____ to get a job

    _____ to better understand American life and culture

    _____ to get a better job; my present job is _____

    _____ to go to college/university

B. Note of Excuse for a School Absence

Mrs. Chin's daughter, Amy, was sick with the flu for two days and could not attend class in her fourth grade. She had a high temperature and threw up several times. Mrs. Chin took her to the doctor and now she is OK and ready to go back to school. Mrs. Chin now must write a note to the teacher, Mrs. Henderson, explaining why Amy wasn't in class.

_____

_____

_____

_____

_____

_____

_____

_____

C. Examination Directions

Answer Sheet

	a	b	c	d
1.	0	0	0	●
2.	0	0	0	●

Test Booklet

1. What time will it be in fifteen minutes?
   - a. 4:30
   - c. 4:00
   - b. 7:30
   - d. 4:15

2. What does this sign mean?
   - a. Stop
   - c. Danger
   - b. Go in
   - d. Go out this door

EXIT

DIRECTIONS

1. Please do not write in the test booklet. Mark answers only on the answer sheet by filling in the correct circle: a, b, c or d.

2. Read and follow all directions carefully.

3. Use number 2 pencil only. No ink.

4. Try to answer each question. Choose the one best answer.

5. If you change an answer, be sure to erase the first mark completely.

6. Be sure to write your name on the answer sheet.

7. You have forty minutes to answer the questions. The instructor will announce to the class when there are five minutes left.

Exercise L-1:

1. Where do you write your name? _____

2. How and where do you write the answer? _____ _____

3. Can you use a ballpoint pen? _____

4. Can a question have more than one possible answer? _____

5. Should you work slowly? _____

6. How will you know that it's almost the end of the test? _____ _____

7. Nelson wrote an answer and then changed his mind. Is this the correct way to do it? _____

```
a   b   c   d
X   0   ●   0
```

8. Susan solved one of the math problems by doing the computation in the test booklet. Was this OK? If not, what should she have done? _____

9. What's wrong with Adam's answer? _____ _____

```
a   b   c   d
0   ●   0   ●
```

IX. Problem Solving

Mr. and Mrs. Turnson have two children, Mark, who's a senior in high school and Karen, who's a junior. Mark doesn't like school and prefers to work on cars with his friends. Karen is a straight A honor student who has a dream of becoming a doctor. Mr. Turnson wants his boy to go to the same university that he went to and become a lawyer in his well-known firm. He thinks that Karen should think about getting married to a young man with a promising career and not follow a career which he thinks is too difficult for her. Mrs. Turnson is very shy and lets her husband make all the decisions in the family, but she feels sympathy with her daughter's dream.

A. What is the problem? _____ _____

B. What are all the possible solutions? _____ _____ _____

C. Which is the best solution? _____ _____

UNIT 11

LAW

It's almost impossible for an adult to live in this country without a basic knowledge of the laws of the land. The legal system isn't just for judges and lawyers; it is for the common person. Although we don't want to face the law in a difficult situation, it still might be necessary in the future for each of us either to have sufficient knowledge of our laws or to know how to find legal help.

Objectives

Competencies:
  Finding Legal Advice
  Traffic Ticket
  Legal Rights
  City Ordinance
  Legal Form

Structure:
  Relative Clauses
  Wish Verbs

Pronunciation:
  long o (ō)
  long o (ō) / (aw)
  SH / S and Z / J

I. Vocabulary

A. Court System

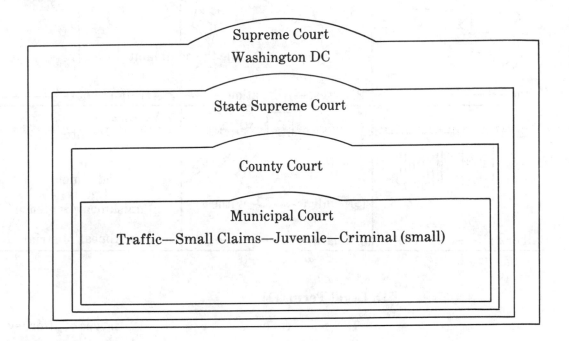

Supreme Court
Washington DC

State Supreme Court

County Court

Municipal Court
Traffic—Small Claims—Juvenile—Criminal (small)

B. Courtroom

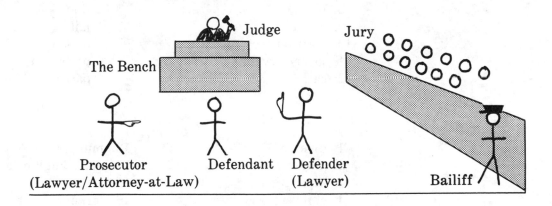

Judge

Jury

The Bench

Prosecutor
(Lawyer/Attorney-at-Law)

Defendant

Defender
(Lawyer)

Bailiff

C. Process

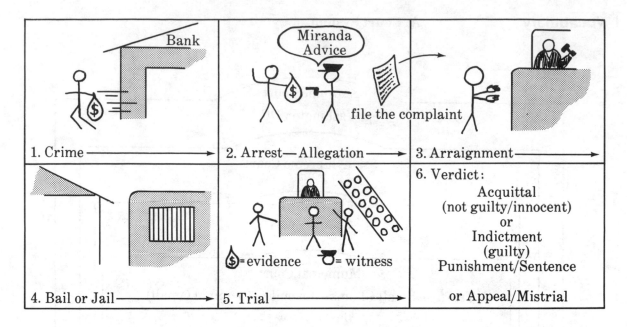

1. Crime ⟶ 2. Arrest—Allegation ⟶ 3. Arraignment ⟶

file the complaint

Miranda Advice

4. Bail or Jail ⟶ 5. Trial ⟶ 6. Verdict:
Acquittal
(not guilty/innocent)
or
Indictment
(guilty)
Punishment/Sentence

or Appeal/Mistrial

$ = evidence   = witness

D. Legal Terms (1)

1. misdemeanor
2. felony
3. civil action
4. criminal action
5. summons
6. charge
7. hearing
8. plea
9. waive
10. warrant
11. juror/jury duty
12. oath

13. power of attorney
14. sue/file suit/damages
15. custody
16. accessory
17. accomplice
18. witness/testify
19. sentence:
    fine
    jail
    prison
    probation
    parole

E. Legal Terms (2)

1. divorce
2. alimony
3. separation
4. child support
5. custody
6. rape
7. assault
8. larceny
9. robbery
10. burglary
11. theft
12. homicide

13. murder
14. manslaughter
15. arson
16. forgery
17. embezzlement
18. bankruptcy
19. residency
20. citizenship/naturalization
21. deportation
22. illegal alien
23. capital punishment

224

F. The Miranda Advice

You are under arrest. You have the right to remain silent. You are not required to say anything to us at any time or to answer any questions. Anything you say can be used against you in court. You have the right to talk to a lawyer for advice before we question you and to have him with you during questioning. If you cannot afford a lawyer and want one, a lawyer will be provided for you. If you want to answer any questions now without a lawyer present, you will still have the right to stop answering at any time until you talk to a lawyer.

II. Getting Started

A. Supreme Court

B. Local Court

Picture A

1. Describe what's in the picture.
2. What kind of problems are presented in this court?
3. Is there a Supreme Court in your native country? If yes, where is it located and what kind of problems are presented there?

Picture B

1. Describe what's in the picture.
2. What kind of problems are presented in this court?
3. Are there local courts in your native country and if so, what kinds of problems do they handle?

Pictures A and B

1. Point out those things that are similar and those things that are different in these pictures.
2. Lolita got a traffic ticket for driving over the speed limit. She didn't understand what the police said to her because she was so nervous and when she got home she realized that she had lost the ticket. What should she do?

III. Conversation

A.

1. I hear that you have to go to court next week.
2. That's right. It's an immigration hearing for my cousin.

1. Do you have a good lawyer?
2. No, I don't know very much about the legal system here or how to find a good lawyer that I can trust.

1. There are plenty of places where you can get all the information you need, especially concerning legal assistance.
2. That's great. I was afraid that my cousin wouldn't be able to find someone competent to represent him.

1. Well, you'd better get to work on it right away.
2. OK, I will. Thanks a lot for your advice.

1. Here's a list of places and telephone numbers. Don't hesitate to call them.
2. I see that one of them is in the library. I think I'll stop by on my way home.

B.

1. Did you read about that big homicide case in the city?
2. I couldn't help but read about it. The news was all over. It was really terrible.

1. There seem to be murders everywhere nowadays. The crime rate seems to keep going higher.
2. There are quite a few people around with mental problems. And of course there are a lot of guns.

1. That's true. It's the easiest thing in the world to buy a gun.
2. A friend of my cousin got mugged the other night as he was coming out of the movie theater.

1. Really? I tell you, the streets aren't as safe as they used to be.
2. I guess you just have to be more careful when you go out now.

1. Well, let's hope everything will be better. It's pretty quiet here in this part of town.
2. Yes, I agree with you on that.

226

C.

1. I went to small claims court last week.
2. What's that all about?

1. It's a court to hear cases concerning moderate amounts of money. There are no lawyers. A judge listens to both sides of the argument and makes a decision right there.
2. You mean there are no complicated formalities and procedures?

1. That's right. It's very simple.
2. Sounds like something that anybody can use. What do you have to do to arrange everything?

1. Just pay a small fee and fill out a form with your complaint.
2. That's simple. Then you are assigned a day to go there, right?

1. Yes. In my case, the dry cleaners ruined my good coat and they only offered me a small sum in exchange.
2. So you're going to try and make them repay you a larger amount for their mistake.

1. That's right.
2. Well, I wish you the best of luck.

Dialogue Puzzle: With a partner fill in the appropriate responses or questions in the spaces of the dialogue below, then practice and read to the rest of the class.

1. I got a ticket the other day.
2. _____

1. I was driving ten miles an hour over the speed limit.
2. _____

1. _____
2. That's a lot of money to pay. Why didn't you go to traffic school instead?

1. _____
2. Traffic violations are a pain in the neck, but we have to have safety laws.

1. My friend witnessed a hit-and-run accident in front of her house. Thank goodness the police caught the guy who did it.
2. _____

1. Small traffic and parking tickets aren't that bad. Everyone makes mistakes.
2. _____

Discussion: Answer the following questions about things talked about in the previous conversations.

1. Have you or anyone you know ever received a traffic ticket?
2. Have you ever witnessed or seen an accident?
3. Have you or anyone you know ever needed a lawyer?

IV. Reading

A. Vocabulary

testify	go on	pedestrian	loading zone
damages	fiancée	city hall	work out
mugger	cable	witness	requirements
snap	out front	tripped	hurriedly

B. Reading

Mohammed Raka was a refugee of the war that was going on in his native country of Afghanistan. He escaped to the United States and now lives with his brother, who is planning to marry.

One day Mohammed's brother and his fiancée went to city hall to find out the requirements for a marriage license. Mohammed decided to go to a downtown restaurant for lunch by himself. When he arrived there he sat down at a table by the window and started reading the newspaper, which had a headline article about a mugger attacking an old woman.

When the waiter brought the menu, a truck parked in the loading zone out front. The driver took a long cable out of the truck, pulled it into the restaurant, and started to talk to the waiter. Just then a woman in a long fur coat and a red hat walked hurriedly along the sidewalk. When she came to the cable, she tripped and fell down. She held her wrist with a painful expression as she got up. She looked inside the restaurant and snapped, "Hey, what's the big idea!"

The waiter called the owner from the kitchen. The short fat man in a dark suit apologized to the woman but she was still angry. "I'm going to sue you. That cable is dangerous for pedestrians."

"Take it easy," the owner said. "I'm sure we can work this out."

The woman rubbed her wrist and said, "It's probably broken." Then she turned around and pointed to Mohammed and said, "He's my witness. He saw everything."

Mohammed was both surprised and nervous. The owner finally said, "Here, will $100 be enough for damages?" The woman grabbed the large bill and smiled. As she left the restaurant, she stopped by Mohammed's table and kissed him on the cheek. "Thanks a lot," she said with a wink. Then she quickly disappeared.

Mohammed's cheeks turned red. Life is sometimes quite unpredictable, he thought to himself.

C. Exercises

1. Put these sentences in the correct time sequence of the story using a 1 for what came first, all the way to 7 as last.

   _____ a. Mohammed arrived in the United States.

   _____ b. The woman in the red hat tripped and fell.

   _____ c. The waiter gave Mohammed the menu.

   _____ d. The owner of the restaurant said he was sorry.

   _____ e. The truck driver dragged the cable into the restaurant.

   _____ f. The woman took the money from the owner.

   _____ g. Mohammed heard that he was going to be a witness.

2. Write *true* or *false*.

   _____ a. Mohammed's brother was single.

   _____ b. Mohammed read about sports in the newspaper.

   _____ c. The truck out front parked in a loading zone.

   _____ d. The woman tripped over a box.

   _____ e. The restaurant owner apologized to the woman.

   _____ f. The woman was seriously hurt.

   _____ g. Mohammed was bored the whole time in the restaurant.

3. Write the vocabulary words from Section A (page 228) in the blank spaces.

   a. How long did the party _____ ?

   b. The mayor, realizing she was late, _____
      walked up the steps to her office in _____ .

   c. The _____ to the homicide will _____
      at the trial.

   d. The police finally caught and arrested the _____ .

   e. The man _____ on the toy but didn't
      fall down.

   f. At the trial, the court awarded her $5,000 in _____ .

   g. He walked with his attractive _____
      across the street in the _____ crossing.

   h. They parked _____ in the _____ .

   i. They will have to _____ all the details
      in the contract.

   j. What are the _____ for that job?

   k. Did he _____ up his jacket before
      going out?

   l. There should be another _____ attached
      to the TV.

229

V. Structure

Relative Clauses

Relative clauses, sometimes called adjective clauses, are clauses that describe or modify nouns. They also put two ideas into one sentence.

Sentence 1:

The lawyer is waiting outside.

Sentence 2:

The lawyer talked with you on the phone yesterday.

Sentence with relative clause. (Who is the relative pronoun.)

The lawyer who talked with you on the phone yesterday is waiting outside.

Relative clauses usually begin with relative pronouns that act as:

1. Subject: who or that for persons; that or which for things.

   (person)

   > The judge who heard the case will be there.
   > The Italians that visited the school are attorneys.

   (thing)

   > The book that explains the criminal codes is there.
   > The case which has been in the news is in that courtroom.

2. Object of verb: who, whom or that for persons; which or that for things.

   (person)

   > The person who(m) you should see is Mr. King.
   > I phoned the immigration lawyer that you talked about.

   (thing)

   > My cousin owns the cement company that I told you about.
   > He complained about the sentence that he got.

3. Object of preposition: whom for persons; which for things.

   (person)

   > I spoke with the man for whom they had the party.

   (thing)

   > She talked about the lawyer's services for which she had paid more than twenty thousand dollars.

Exercise S-1: Write in a correct relative pronoun, <u>who, whom, that</u> or <u>which.</u>

1. The oath _____ he took was a normal part of the procedure.
2. I talked with the witness _____ had seen the assault.
3. The defender _____ was always complaining finally left.
4. She knows the judge with _____ you talked.
5. The form for filing for a suit _____ you are referring to is out of date.

Exercise S-2: Combine the two sentences, making the one in parentheses a relative clause.

Examples:

The theft (The theft was in the newspapers) happened near school.
The theft that was in the newspaper happened near school.

I like the program (you told me about the program).
I like the program that you told me about.

1. Do you want to hire a lawyer (a lawyer specializes in child support)?

   _____

   _____

2. The man (the man lost $5,000 in the robbery) is moving to Texas.

   _____

   _____

3. Everyone (everyone has met him) seems to like him a lot.

   _____

   _____

4. Bob talked to a policeman (a policeman explained the Miranda advice). _____

   _____

5. Where are the papers (you ordered the papers)?

   _____

   _____

6. Is that the divorce lawyer (your neighbor hired the divorce lawyer)?

   _____

   _____

7. The office (I used to have the office) was much bigger than this.

_____

_____

8. I met the student (she told me about the student).

_____

_____

Relative clauses sometimes begin with the possessive adjective <u>whose.</u>

That is the man. The man's picture was in the paper.
That is the man <u>whose picture was in the paper.</u>

I read about the company. The company's books are in the red.
I read about the company <u>whose books are in the red.</u>

Exercise S-3: Change the sentence in parentheses to a relative clause with <u>whose.</u>

1. The law office (the law office's secretaries are bilingual) is moving.

_____

_____

2. Do you know the bailiff (the bailiff's responsibility is to keep order in the court)? _____

_____

Relative clauses sometimes begin with the adverbs <u>when, where</u> or <u>why</u>.

This is the year <u>when the conference is in Los Angeles.</u>
That is the neighborhood <u>where I live.</u>
I don't know the reason <u>why she said that.</u>

Exercise: Write your own relative clauses by finishing these sentences.

1. Do you know the day when _____ ?
2. I like a city where _____ .
3. I understand the reason why _____ .

Relative clauses can be restrictive or nonrestrictive. The clause is restrictive when it identifies the noun it describes and it is necessary for the sentence's meaning.

The man who committed the felony is my neighbor.

A relative clause is nonrestrictive when the clause just adds information about the noun but it isn't necessary for the sentence's meaning. It is separated from the rest of the sentence by commas.

My brother John, who lives in Hayward, visited me last night.

<u>That</u> cannot replace <u>who, whom</u> or <u>which</u> in nonrestrictive clauses.

Exercise S-4: Mark the relative clause with commas if it is nonrestrictive.

1. His sister who is in college speaks three languages.
2. His uncle who lives in Denver is his mother's brother.
3. The secretary who explained it to you left a few things out.
4. Mrs. Hogan who was the bookkeeper before is the new receptionist.
5. The apartment that you liked has a vacant studio.
6. Jasper's Electronics which is located near the freeway has an excellent reputation for well-made products.

Relative pronoun objects that, who(m), and which are not necessary in restrictive clauses and can be left out.

The man (that) you talked to is my classmate.

Also, who, which or that plus the verb to be can usually be left out.

The person (who is) talking is Mr. Smith.

Which and who(m) cannot be left out in nonrestrictive clauses.

Ms. Cameron, whom you met before, is giving the main speech.

Exercise: Write in relative clauses or main clauses using your own words.

1. Bob, _____ , told me about the robbery.
2. I know about the arson _____ .
3. _____ , who recently got a divorce, _____ .
4. The man _____ was arrested for being an accomplice in the bank robbery.
5. Many people _____ will go to trial.
6. _____ , whose brother is a lawyer, _____ .
7. I like the hotel _____ .
8. I don't know the reason _____ .
9. I remember the year _____ .
10. I bought a new car _____ .

Wish Verbs

<u>Wish</u> usually indicates a condition that is contrary to fact, not present or impossible. For a present action, use a past tense clause after the verb <u>wish,</u> using the same rule of the verb <u>to be</u> as in the condition (I were, he were, etc.) or a past auxiliary plus a present verb for the future.

> I wish I <u>knew</u> more about the laws.
> He wishes he <u>were</u> a judge.
> My friend wishes that she <u>could go</u> home this year.

For past action after wish, use the past perfect tense, or past auxiliary plus have plus the past participle.

> They wish they <u>had</u> <u>not</u> <u>sued</u> the doctor last year.
> She wished that she <u>could</u> <u>have</u> <u>gone</u> home last year.

Exercise S-5: Write the correct form of the verbs following wish.

1. (be) Joe wishes that he _____ a juror.
2. (can) I wish I _____ help you but I can't.
3. (have) Mr. Carlson wishes that he _____ today off. He'd go to the park and relax.
4. (not rain) We all wish that it _____ yesterday.
5. (be) I wish that it _____ yesterday.
6. (visit) He wishes he _____ you next year.
7. (have) They wish they _____ last Sunday off. They'd have gone for a hike.
8. (study) I wish that I _____ harder when I was younger.
9. (not commit) He wished that he _____ the crime.
10. (live) I wish I _____ nearer to my job.

The expressions <u>I</u> <u>wish</u> <u>I</u> <u>could</u> and <u>I</u> <u>wish</u> <u>you</u> <u>wouldn't</u> are used to show polite commands and requests.

> <u>I</u> <u>wish</u> <u>you</u> <u>would</u> tell us more about your native country.
> <u>I</u> <u>wish</u> <u>you</u> <u>wouldn't</u> smoke here.

Exercise S-6: Change these imperative sentences into the above wish requests or commands.

Example:

Come back in 15 minutes.

I wish you would come back in 15 minutes.

1. Help me carry these suitcases.

   _____

2. Don't make any errors.

   _____

3. Take this message.

   _____

Wish is also used in these expressions:

I wish you luck.

We wish them the best.

Note the difference between hope and wish. Hope is for things that seem possible, wish isn't.

He hopes that he can get a job.

He wishes that he could get a job.

Exercise S-7: Choose the correct forms in parentheses.

1. He _____ that he _____ home,
      (wishes/hopes)   (can go/could go)
   but he can't.

2. They _____ they _____ to
       (hope/wish)   (will be able/were able)
   visit her soon. It seems likely.

VI. Composition

Write in the words of your own choice in the spaces, using the words in parentheses below each space as guidelines.

The legal system in the United States is _____ .
                                            (adjective)
One thing about it that I don't understand is _____ .
                                            (noun)
The laws here are _____ because _____
                   (adjective)   (sentence)
_____ . I think that a man who is a judge must be _____ . Lawyers in the United States
                       (adjective)
seem to be _____ . It's _____ to
              (adjective)   (easy/hard)
find a good lawyer.

The legal system in my native country is _____ .
                                        (adjective)
People need lawyers mostly for _____ .
                             (law service)
The judges in my native country are _____ . To be
                              (adjective)
a lawyer a person must _____ .
                         (sentence)
Trials usually last _____ .
                   (how long)
The crime that seems to happen the most in the United States is
_____ . The worst kind of crime is
          (name of crime)
_____ . To prevent the crime of _____
   (name of crime)   (kind of crime)
from happening, a person must _____
                                  (sentence)
_____ . In my native country the most often committed crime is _____ .

The punishment for criminals in the United States is _____ while in my native country it is _____ .

VII. Pronunciation

A. Vowel

long o (ō)

1. par**o**le
   pr**o**bation
   z**o**ne

2. fel**o**ny
   alim**o**ny
   bur**eau**

3. cust**o**dy
   n**o**te
   oak

4. Tomorr**ow** the **ow**ner will kn**ow** the area c**o**de of his ph**o**ne.

5. He br**o**ke a b**o**ne near his elb**ow**.

Contrasts:

long o (ō) / (aw)

6. so/saw
   low/law
   coal/call

7. owe/awe
   flow/flaw
   shoal/shawl

8. hole/hall
   mole/mall
   goal/gall

B. Consonant:

SH / S and Z / J

1. **sh**ed/**s**aid
   shore/**s**ore
   fa**sh**ion/fa**s**ten
   plu**sh**/plu**s**

2. **z**est/**j**est
   zone/**J**oan
   pay**s**/pa**g**e
   rain**s**/ran**g**e

3. The **s**ingle **s**on lea**s**ed the **s**ame me**ss**y **sh**ack.

4. The hu**ge** carriage **z**i**gz**a**gg**ed in the rain**s**.

VIII. Life Skills

A. Legal Advice

Exercise L-1: 1. Check those situations when you may need or want a lawyer or other legal help.

a. _____ You are charged with a crime.

b. _____ You apply for a driver's license.

c. _____ You have been seriously injured.

d. _____ You are going to sell or buy a house or other real estate.

e. _____ You register for school.

f. _____ You are going to sign a contract that you don't understand.

g. _____ You get a divorce.

h. _____ You get a new job.

i. _____ You are charged with drunken or reckless driving.

j. _____ You pay your telephone bill late.

k. _____ Someone is suing you.

2. Read the different ways to find a lawyer, then read the descriptions of the people and decide which way would be the best way to get a lawyer.

a. A relative, friend or acquaintance is a lawyer or can recommend one.

b. The company has a lawyer for its employees.

c. The Lawyer Referral Service in the yellow pages of the phone directory recommends one for your special problem for a fee.

d. The yellow pages lists the names of lawyers.

e. The Legal Aid Society finds free legal help for people with little money, but not for criminal cases.

f. For criminal cases, the government provides a public defender for no fee.

_____ John is new in the area, is not poor and has a legal problem.

_____ Mary has a small legal problem but she doesn't have a lot of money.

_____ Sue has lived in the area a long time with many relatives and friends and now wants to get a divorce.

_____ Mrs. Johnson has worked for a business firm that takes care of its employees with benefits and special services. She has a contract that she doesn't quite understand.

_____ Harry is charged with a criminal offense but he can't afford a lawyer.

B. Traffic Violation

If already paid, please disregard this notice.
A notice to appear or citation charging a violation of the below described sections has been filed with this court. Unless you appear in court or answer these charges or deposit bail as indicated, you may face further charges, increased bail, arrest, or loss of driving privileges or any combination of such consequences.
Violation: VC-27360A/Child Restraint Device   Date: 6/15/88 Citation No: 46348   Appearance Date: 7/16/88
Bail of $52.00 or reduced bail of $0.00 with Proof-of-Correction may be sent by mail on or before 7/16/88. To appear in court, bring this notice to the court on or before 7/16/88, Monday thru Thursday before 8:30 A.M. Proof-of-Correction must be obtained from a law enforcement officer.
Do not send cash. Make check or money order payable to: Clerk of Municipal Court Central Branch 700 North Delaware St., San Lorenzo, California 97859 Bail payment and/or Proof-of-Correction may be made in person at: 700 North Delaware St., San Lorenzo, California 97859 Hours: 8:00 A.M. to 4 P.M.
Important: This notice must accompany your payment or appearance.

Exercise L-2:

1. What is the violation? _____

   When did it happen? _____

2. How much will it cost without Proof-of-Correction? _____

   With Proof-of-Correction? _____

3. How does a person get a Proof-of-Correction? _____

   _____

4. What should the person do with this notice if he already paid the

   bail? _____

5. The person who receives this notice must answer by what date?

   _____

6. What form of payment can't you send to the court? _____

   _____

C. Legal Rights

If you are arrested, the police must tell you four things before they question you about a crime:

1. You have the right to remain silent.

2. Anything you say may be used against you.

3. You have the right to have a lawyer present when you are questioned.

4. If you can't afford a lawyer, you have the right to free legal help.

It is recommended that if arrested you should:

1. be polite

2. not talk

3. get a lawyer (ask for a free one if you can't afford one)

If a person is arrested in your native country, does the person arrested have the same rights as the above cases? _____

_____

_____

D. City Ordinances

Exercise L-3:

No Bicycles or Skateboard Riding on Sidewalk 13.52.100 C.O. 13.54.010 C.O.

1. Where would you find this city ordinance sign? _____ _____

2. Who is it for? _____ _____

3. Why did they pass an ordinance like this one? _____ _____

4. Another city doesn't have this ordinance. Why not? _____ _____

E. Contracts

A contract is a promise or agreement between two or more parties (persons or groups of persons) to do or not to do something. For a contract to be legal, it must have four conditions.

1. All parties must be competent (to know right from wrong and realize what they are doing) and able to make the contract.
2. All parties must want the contract, one offering something, the other accepting, and an exchange is made.
3. All parties in the contract must get something, that is, there must be consideration where each party gives up something.
4. The contract must be for something legal.

Exercise L-4: Write the number of the condition absent that makes each case not a contract.

_____ a. Mr. Harrison gives his neighbor his old car for free.

_____ b. Frank sells Jason, who is a slow learner, his expensive stereo.

_____ c. Barry and Ann Silver offer $150,000 for the house of their dreams.

_____ d. Mary signed a lease for an apartment where she stored many illegal drugs.

When all four conditions are present and the contract is signed by both parties, then the contract is binding, which means all parties must do what they promised in the contract.

Exercise: You write an ad in the newspaper to sell your car, a 1984 Toyota Tercel, for $3,000. Alice Gasper arrives and says that she wants to buy the car but she will pay you tomorrow. What should you do?

_____ 1. Tell her to come back tomorrow with the money.

_____ 2. Say no because she might not go through with it.

_____ 3. Write down the terms of the agreement and have her sign her name next to yours.

_____ 4. Have a neighbor listen to her agreement to buy the car so that you'd have proof of what she said.

_____ 5. Have Alice check the car over with you so that she understands what she is buying.

IX. Problem Solving

Mrs. Farmington's husband is an alcoholic. Many times when he gets drunk, he'll come home and beat her. He drinks because he says he feels a lot of pressure at his job and has failed to get a promotion in the last five years. Each time he attacks her, he gets more violent. They have two small children. What should she do?

A. What is the problem? _____

_____

_____

_____

B. What are all the possible solutions? _____

_____

_____

_____

C. Which is the best solution? _____

_____

_____

_____

UNIT 12

POST OFFICE

The services at the post office are many, whether it's delivering mail, issuing important government forms, selling money orders, or sending off packages. This unit will cover the various aspects of the postal system as they relate to the language of the ordinary customer.

Objectives

Competencies:
Money Order
Change of Address Form
Address an Envelope
Letter

Structure:
Interjections
Punctuation:
   Periods
   Question Marks
   Exclamation Marks
   Commas
   Semicolons
   Colons

Pronunciation:
(aw)
(aw) / (ow)
L / N and NG / N

I. Vocabulary

A. Post Office

1. mailbox
2. letter slot
3. sender
4. addressee
5. post office box (P.O. Box)
6. envelope
7. airmail
8. special delivery
9. insured mail
10. registered mail
11. first class, regular
12. second class, newspapers, periodicals
13. third class, advertising, "junk" mail
14. fourth class, package, parcel post
15. express mail
16. postal clerk
17. postal service
18. postage
19. stamp, sheet of stamps
20. postmark
21. letter carrier, mailman, mailwoman
22. postcard
23. handling
24. correspondence
25. cash on delivery (COD)
26. money order
27. return address
28. ounce (28.4 grams), pound (16 ounces)

B. Verbs

1. send, mail
2. register
3. certify
4. deliver
5. weigh
6. collect
7. return, send back
8. forward
9. hold

II. Getting Started

A.

B.

Picture A

1. Describe what's in the picture.
2. Why would you mail a letter here?
3. How do the post offices here compare with those in your native country?

Picture B

1. Describe what's in the picture.
2. Why would you mail a letter here?
3. How do mail boxes here compare with those in your native country?

Pictures A and B

1. Point out those things that are the same and those that are different in these pictures.
2. Joan is returning a letter for an important job offer. Where should she mail it?

243

III. Conversation

A.

C = Customer   P = Postal Clerk

C: I want to send this package to New York. I really had a hard time wrapping it properly.

P: It weighs a little over a pound. How do you want to send it?

C: First class.

P: Do you want to insure it?

C: I don't know. Is it expensive?

P: Not really. Here's a table of all the rates. Yours would be this.

C: Oh, that's not bad. You know, it's important that this package gets there. I think I'll insure it for that amount.

P: Fine. (Takes money.) And here's your change.

C: When will it get there?

P: Probably on Friday.

C: Thank you.

P: You're welcome. Have a nice day.

B.

1. Excuse me, could you please tell me where the nearest mailbox is?
2. Yes, it's halfway down this block, right in front of the school. You can't miss it.

1. Is it red and white?
2. No, that's a fire alarm box. The mailbox is blue.

1. Oh, I see. And where is the post office located?
2. That's downtown. It's about a fifteen-minute walk or a two-minute drive. The mail goes faster when you drop it off at the post office. They pick up the mail only at five in the afternoon at the mailboxes.

1. Thank you very much.
2. I'm glad I could be of some help.

C.

1. I was thinking of sending a pearl necklace to my mother for her birthday.
2. You'd better send it by registered mail.

1. Why's that?
2. It's the safest way to send your valuables.

1. That's important to know. One other thing—I'm always running out of stamps.
2. Why not buy a book of stamps?

1. I didn't realize they had them.
2. It'll surely save you a lot of trips to the post office.

Dialogue Puzzle: With a partner fill in the appropriate responses and questions in the spaces of the dialogue below, then practice and read to the class.

1. _____
2. To the post office.

1. _____
2. I have to get one of those change of address forms.

1. When do you plan to be moving?
2. _____

1. Do you usually get a lot of mail?
2. _____

1. _____
2. Sure, I don't mind buying them for you while I'm there.

1. _____
2. Yeah, and I'm going to miss you as a neighbor after we move.

Discussion: Answer the following questions about things talked about in the previous conversations.

1. What did you do the last time you went to the post office?
2. Do you feel that the mail service here is reliable?
3. Who is the last person you wrote a letter to?
4. What's the difference between stamps in your native country and here?
5. What sort of mail really delights you?
6. What kind of mail is disappointing?

IV. Reading

A. Vocabulary

fraud	accused	valuables	bulletin board
zone	awful	grin	smiles from ear to ear
midst	glance	exchange	post office box
uneasy	out loud	authentic	concerning

B. Reading

Michiyo parked in the ten-minute zone in front of the post office, got out of her car, and went in. She then waited at the end of the long line. After glancing around the room she began to read the criminal notices on the bulletin board. She noticed one man accused of mail fraud who looked like her English teacher at the adult school. She laughed to herself.

245

Just then one of her classmates, Juan, walked in. They exchanged greetings and talked for a little while. Then Michiyo asked what she had missed in class the two days this week when she was home with her sick child. Juan told her about the lesson concerning the post office.

"Well," she said, "maybe you can check to see if I use the correct English when I try to send this package. I'm sending my nephew some authentic blue jeans made in the USA."

"We practiced using English in a lot of different situations in the post office," Juan answered. "Buying stamps, changing your address, sending a package or valuables, or a special delivery letter—but you know, I always get uneasy when I'm using English in a real situation."

"Are you here to send something?" Michiyo asked.

"No, I'm picking up the mail in my uncle's post office box, and I'm hoping that I'll get a letter from my girlfriend back in my native country. She always puts a lot of perfume on whatever she writes—it drives me crazy."

Michiyo grinned and then asked him about the upcoming class party. Then Juan said goodbye and hurried off to check his mail. A few minutes later Michiyo was in the midst of sending her package when Juan passed by, sniffing a letter in a pink envelope, smiling from ear to ear. As she laughed out loud, the clerk looked up and asked her, "Is there anything wrong?"

"Oh, no, nothing at all," she replied, feeling a little embarrassed.

C. Exercises

1. Write these sentences in the correct time sequence of the story, using a 1 for what came first all the way to 7 as last.

    _____ a. Michiyo spotted Juan sniffing the letter.

    _____ b. Juan opened his uncle's post office box.

    _____ c. Michiyo parked.

    _____ d. Michiyo noticed the bulletin board.

    _____ e. The clerk asked if anything was wrong.

    _____ f. Michiyo waited at the end of the long line.

    _____ g. The post office opened.

2. Write *true* or *false*.

    _____ a. Michiyo's parking place was for an unlimited time.

    _____ b. Criminals' posters are sometimes located in the post office.

    _____ c. The post office was busy.

    _____ d. Michiyo had perfect attendance at English class.

    _____ e. Her class had been studying about banks recently.

    _____ f. Juan was married.

    _____ g. Juan left the post office disappointed because he did not get a letter.

3. Vocabulary: Put the vocabulary words from Section A (page 245) in the spaces.

   a. She left her _____ in the safe deposit box.

   b. There was an _____ lot of information _____ the new scientific discovery in the newspaper.

   c. I felt _____ about accepting the invitation. I wasn't comfortable.

   d. Did you _____ at the notes on the _____ ?

   e. He _____ me of parking in an emergency _____ .

   f. The nations had a friendly cultural _____ .

   g. My friend always _____ when he eats _____ Chinese food.

   h. I'll pick up the mail at my _____ very soon.

   i. They are in the _____ of a trial regarding mail _____ .

   j. He read the letter _____ .

V. Structure

| Punctuation |
| Periods | . |

A. Use a period after a complete thought with a subject and verb, and also an indirect question.

   They mailed the letter early.

   Have your money ready.

   They wanted to know if your cousin had picked up the package.

B. Use periods: after initials and abbreviations; to separate dollars and cents; after numbers and letters in an outline (as on this page).

   Dr.   Ave.   P.M. $38.17

C. Use three periods in a series within a sentence and four at the end to show omission or something left out. (It is also called an elipsis.)

   Gary drove his friends to the post office yesterday.

   Gary drove . . . to the post office yesterday.

   Gary drove his friends . . .

247

Commas ,

A. Use commas before a coordinating conjunction in a compound sentence.

> He checked the letter, but he couldn't find anything wrong.

B. Use a comma like a pause especially after an introductory or dependent phrase or clause.

> Since you came early, I'll show you the postcards I've got.
> As the plane started to take off, the rain poured.

C. Use commas to set off phrases or clauses that are not necessary to the meaning of the sentence, or words especially added.

> The post office branch, which opened four years ago, has very good service.
> David Razo, our mail carrier, lives nearby.
> No, I've never been there.

D. Use commas in addresses, letters and dates.

> Thursday, October 13, 1986
> 1516 Carol Ave., Richmond, California
> Dear Eric,
> Sincerely,

E. Use commas to separate words, phrases or clauses in a series.

> They received two letters, a postcard, and some junk mail.
> She got up, ate breakfast, got ready, and went to work.

F. Use a comma before an informal direct quotation.

> Gloria asked, "Where is the nearest mailbox?"

Question Marks ?

A. Use a question mark after a direct question or a series of questions.

> What is the price for sending a package first class?
> How long have you been waiting? Five minutes? Fifteen? Twenty?

Note: Use a period after a request that is in question form.

> Will you please send me the bill.

Semicolons ;

Semicolons are between a comma, which indicates a pause, and a period, which indicates a full stop.

A. Use a semicolon between clauses of a compound sentence when there is no conjunction.

> The emergency lights were flashing; no one knew what to do.

B. Use a semicolon sometimes to make clear numbers and other items in a list.

   The rates are: $10.40; $7.80; $6.95; and $4.35.

C. Use a semicolon in a list of equal parts that also require commas.

   He traveled to Denver, Colorado; Springfield, Illinois; Johnstown, Pennsylvania; and Salt Lake City, Utah.

| Colons | : |

A. Use a colon to introduce a list after such words as <u>the following,</u> <u>as follows,</u> etc.

   You should have the following in your desk: stamps, envelopes writing paper, and a pen.

B. Use a colon after a business salutation.

   Dear Sirs:

   To Whom It May Concern:

C. Use a colon to introduce a formal quotation.

   The world leader, in his speech to the United Nations, said: "It is time for peace . . . "

| Exclamation Points | ! |

A. Use an exclamation point after an expression or statement of strong feeling.

   Wow!

   We want peace now!

| Quotation Marks | " " |

A. Use quotation marks to enclose a speaker's exact words.

   The postal clerk said, "We're out of those stamps."

B. Use quotation marks to enclose special expressions, titles of magazines, book chapters, essays, stories or poems from a larger work.

   The man said that the news was a lot of "bull."

   The article, "Immigration," was in last week's issue of *Time*.

C. Use single quotation marks for quotations within other quotations.

   The mail carrier said, "I didn't understand you when you said, 'I'm going on vacation in three days.' "

| Apostrophes | ' |

A. Use an apostrophe for possession.

   the person's money order

   the letter's return address

B. Use an apostrophe for a contraction.

> I'd   he's   she won't

C. Use an apostrophe for the plural of a letter or number.

> Write all your b's clearly.
>
> There are many 18's here.

Dashes — —

A. Use a dash within a sentence to indicate a break in thought such as an expression that is separated from or just added to the main idea of the sentence.

> The truck will be there—no sooner, no later—to pick up the mail.
>
> The package—the one they've been talking about—finally arrived.

B. Use a dash to introduce a phrase that summarizes the preceding part of the sentence.

> Drunk driving, fatigue, neglect—these are all causes of serious auto accidents.

Hyphens -

A. Use a hyphen in compound numbers from twenty-one to ninety-nine.

B. Use a hyphen in a compound noun or adjective.

> brother-in-law   well-known

C. Use a hyphen to separate words at the end of the line, dividing at the syllable. Do not divide a proper name or leave a single letter on a line alone.

Parentheses ( )

A. Use parentheses to set off a part of the sentence that is not necessary to the meaning of the sentence.

> The two countries agreed to continue studying their mail service problems (according to both news agencies).

Capitals

A. Capitalize the first word in every sentence, the first word of the salutation and close in a letter.

> Dear gentlemen:
>
> Yours truly,

B. Capitalize the following:

1) person names

> Martin Luther King

250

2) titles of persons and literary works

    Ms., Dr., Governor, Treasure Island

3) days, months and holidays

    Tuesday, April, Christmas

4) cities, countries, etc.

    Paris, Japan, the Phillipines

5) regions of the country

    the North, the Midwest

6) abbreviations

    P.M., S.O.S., C.O.D.

7) religious, racial and ethnic groups

    Catholic, Caucasian, Asian

8) political parties and governmental bodies

    Democrat, Congress

Exercise S-1: Correct the punctuation errors in each sentence.

1. the freeway between san francisco and los angeles is long straight and sometimes boring

2. bob johnson our dentist lives at 345 elm street smallville ohio

3.   january 7 1987

    dear sirs

    im writing this letter to complain about the service we received at your store in miami john quinn the salesman treated us very badly and the merchandise we bought was defective i hope this doesnt happen again

                    sincerely

                    don smith

4. bob asked how much is it to send a registered letter

5. since you asked ill explain it to you

6. gee that was very close

7. his sister in law is very self centered

8. bobs friend isnt going to new york

9. I enjoyed reading the article The Joy of Cooking in that magazine

10. the problem that I was talking about last week really hasnt gotten any better.

VI. Composition

The Post Office

Write in the words of your own choice in the spaces using the words in parentheses below each space as guidelines.

_____ delivers the mail to my home
(who)

Monday through _____ at about _____ o'clock.
(day)

_____ usually pick(s) up the mail from the
(who in your home)

mailbox. The best kind of mail to get is _____
(kind of mail)

while the worst is _____ . It usually takes
(where you live)

_____ days to get a letter from _____
(where you live)

to _____ .
(where you usually send to)

The closest post office to my home is _____
(blocks or miles)

away. It takes _____ to get there by
(how long)

_____ . I _____ go to the post office
(transportation)   (how often)

because _____ . If I have
(reason)

a letter that is important I _____ .
(where do you mail it)

The postal system in the United States is _____ .
(adjective)

The postal service in my native country is _____ .
(adjective)

_____ delivers the mail _____ through
(who)   (day)

_____ there. The difference between the postal system
(day)

there and here is _____
(sentence)

_____ . Stamps in

my native country are _____ .
(adjective)

VII. Pronunciation

A. Vowel

(aw)

1. call
   office
   haul

2. flaw
   bought
   chalk

3. cost
   caught
   cough

4. They talked about geography during coffee break.

5. They launched the long rocket before dawn in the fall.

Contrasts:

(aw) / (ow)

6.	all/owl	7.	tall/towel	8.	pawn/pound
	fall/foul		hall/howl		drawn/drown
	bought/bout		wrong/round		dawn/down

B. Consonants:

L / N and NG / N

1.	lock/knock	2.	banged/banned
	line/nine		tonges/tons
	slap/snap		rang/ran
	file/fine		long/lawn

3. A slow snow fell on the fine lawn.

4. Those thin things in your hand always ring.

VII. Life Skills   A. Money Orders

UNITED STATES OF AMERICA POSTAL MONEY ORDER	15-20 000
20374562435 860921 115643	**25*00

MONEY ORDER

UNITED STATES POSTAL SERVICE
U.S. MAIL
0198

Void Without
USPS Seal
000910040

Do not stamp, write or mark above this line.

PAY TO
JOHN MILLER

PURCHASED BY
ZACK HEARST

For YARD WORK

20374562435

Dollars and Cents

NOT VALID IF OVER

Twenty-Five
Dollars

USA

Exercise L-1: The post office sells money orders, which are a safe way to send money by mail. The post office fills in the amount you want to send.

1. How much is being sent in the above example?_____

2. Who is sending the money? _____

3. Who will receive it? Why? _____

4. What are some important things to know about this postal money order? _____

Not Negotiable	CUSTOMER'S RECEIPT	Not Negotiable	15-20 000

20374562435	860921	115643	**25*00

Serial Number	Year Month Day	Post Office	Dollars and Cents Amount of Original Money Order

PAY TO *JOHN MILLER*

PURCHASED BY *ZACK HEARST*   Not Negotiable

For *YARD WORK*

This receipt is your guarantee of a 100% refund if your money order is lost or stolen, provided you fill in the Pay To and Purchased By information on the money order in the space provided. If your money order is lost or stolen, present this receipt and file a claim for a refund at your post office. Please allow 60 days before making a claim or inquiry.

5. Who will endorse this or sign his name on the back of the money order? _____

6. How long should the purchaser wait before asking about a lost money order? _____

7. If someone steals the money order, what do you do? _____

_____

B. Change of Address

This order provides for the forwarding of first-class mail and all parcels of obvious value for a period not to exceed 1 year.	Print or Type Name (last, first, middle)

Change of address is for:
☐ Firm
☐ Entire Family (when last names differ, file separate orders)
☐ Individual Signer Only
	OLD ADDRESS:
	    No. and St.
	    Apt., Suite
	    P.O. Box
	    R.D. No. Box

	Post Office State/Zip Code

I agree to pay forward postage for newspapers and magazines for 90 days.
        ☐ No   ☐ Yes
	NEW ADDRESS:
	    No. and St.
	    Apt., Suite
	    P.O. Box
	    R.D. No. Box

USPS Use Only	Post Office State/Zip Code
Clerk/Carrier Endorsement	Effective Date (If temporary, expiration date)
Carrier Route Number	
Date Entered	Signature and title of person authorizing address change. DO NOT PRINT OR TYPE. Sign Here Date Signed
PS Form 3575	

Exercise L-2:

1. How long is this change of address service good for? _____

   _____

2. Linda Garrison lives at 75 Alpine Dr., Apt. #4, in Burlingame, California, zip code 94010. She is moving to 1780 Howard Ave. in the same city. She wants her mail forwarded to the new address starting right away, May 2, 1988. She gets several magazines. How would she fill in this form?

C. Addressing an Envelope

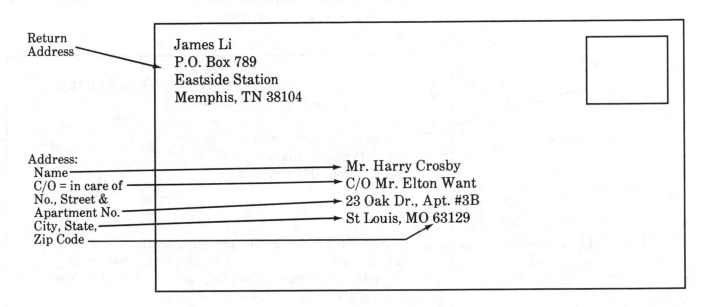

Exercise L-3: On the envelope below, address a letter to Mrs. Karen Bernard, who lives at 48 Elk St., Aurora, Illinois 60505 from yourself.

1. Where do you find zip codes and state abbreviations? _____

_____

2. Why do some letters have in the lower righthand corner, "Do Not Fold or Bend"? Or in letters to a company, "Attention: Mary Lamb"?

_____

_____

D. Writing a Letter

There are different forms of letter writing that have the same six parts: the heading, the inside address, the salutation, the body of the letter, the complimentary close, and the signature.

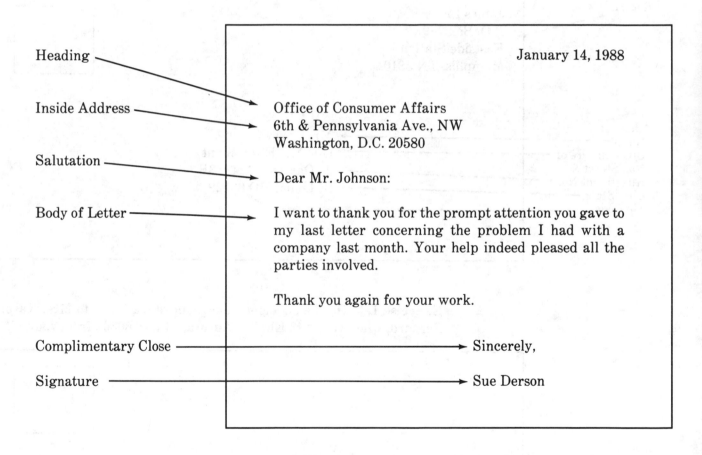

Heading → January 14, 1988

Inside Address → Office of Consumer Affairs
6th & Pennsylvania Ave., NW
Washington, D.C. 20580

Salutation → Dear Mr. Johnson:

Body of Letter → I want to thank you for the prompt attention you gave to my last letter concerning the problem I had with a company last month. Your help indeed pleased all the parties involved.

Thank you again for your work.

Complimentary Close → Sincerely,

Signature → Sue Derson

Heading: This can also include the sender's address.

Inside Address: In informal letters it is not necessary.

Salutation: (formal) Sir: Madam: Dear Sir(s):
(informal) Dear Mrs. Jones: Dear John,

Body of Letter: Paragraphs can have indentation.

Complimentary Close: Sincerely yours, Cordially, Yours truly, Respectfully, Yours gratefully, etc.

Exercise: On a separate sheet of paper write a letter to Mrs. Donna Walters of Geyserville City Hall, 34 Main St., Geyserville, Texas 98879, telling her that you can't go to the big city anniversary dance. Give an excuse.

IX. Problem Solving

Mary walked to the mailbox near her house to mail a letter. On the way back she found a letter on the sidewalk addressed to a house that was a few blocks away. There was no stamp on it and no return address. Out of curiosity she held up the letter to the sunlight and saw some dollar bills. She had some stamps at her house, but there was a suspicious neighbor looking out his window at her. What should she do?

A. What is the problem? _____

_____

_____

B. What are the possible solutions? _____

_____

_____

C. What is the best solution? _____

_____

_____

_____

UNIT 13

MEDIA/ LEISURE TIME

The preceding twelve units have dealt with the essential procedures and customs and vocabulary for functioning effectively in the United States. Leisure time is also important. Recreation has its place, not only easing the mind but providing us with physical exercise. Different kinds of art and entertainment relax us and please us, often feeding the spirit. Through the news media, we get a picture of what is going on in the world and how this affects us.

Objectives

Competencies:
  Newspaper Contents
  Entertainment Guide
  Library Card Catalog

Structure:
  Review

Pronunciation:
  Review

I. Vocabulary

A. Media

Newspaper

1. front page
2. article
3. feature
4. headline
5. column/columnist
6. caption
7. editorial
8. subscription/subscribe
9. newsstand
10. correspondent
11. journalist
12. editor
13. censorship
14. publisher/publish
15. reporter
16. news service/agency
17. press
18. circulation
19. advertisement
20. want ads/classified ads
21. cartoon
22. sections:
    business
    comics
    obituaries
    weather
    sports
    entertainment

Magazine

1. periodical
2. kinds: news, fashion, popular, sports, food, homemaking, science, technical, travel, health, literary . . .

Television

1. channels
2. broadcast/broadcaster
3. announcer
4. rerun
5. station
6. programs: game shows, news, movies, serials, comedies, drama, documentary, special report, children, soap opera, interviews, talk shows, travel, animal, nature/science, cartoon, educational, commercials, sports events, instruction, variety, musical . . .

Other

1. radio
2. VCR (video cassette recorder)
3. earphones
4. stereo
5. music: classical, folk, jazz, popular, blues, romantic, Muzak, choral, rock and roll (light, hard), punk, new wave, country and western, international . . .

B. Entertainment

1. movie theater
2. movie, film, picture, cinema
3. the movies: science fiction, fantasy, special effects, tragedy, comedy, western, adventure, love, mystery . . .
4. theater/drama
5. symphony
6. planetarium
7. aquarium
8. zoo
9. botanical gardens
10. sports event (game, match, tournament)
11. rodeo
12. celebration
13. circus
14. exhibit/exhibition
15. fair
16. parade
17. ballet
18. opera
19. concert
20. performance
21. nightclub
22. museum
23. art gallery
24. historical site
25. tourist attraction
26. musical

C. Books

1. cover
2. title (page)
3. author/writer
4. table of contents
5. preface/introduction/ foreword
6. copyright
7. chapter
8. index
9. hardback
10. pocketbook/softcover
11. fiction
12. non-fiction

13. kinds: novel, short story, poetry, history, self-help, do-it-yourself, mechanics, science, language, classic, best-seller, text, anthology, cooking, religious, medical, psychology . . .
14. bookstore
15. bookshelf
16. bookworm
17. reference: encyclopedia, dictionary, thesaurus
18. library: librarian, main desk, checkout, library card, due date, reference desk, audio-visual department . . .
19. Dewey Decimal System:

Non-Fiction

000-099 General Works	100-199 Philosophy
200-299 Religion	300-399 Social Sciences
400-499 Language	500-599 Pure Science
600-699 Technology	700-799 Arts
800-899 Literature	900-999 History

Fiction

Author's last name	Biography B

II. Getting Started

A.

B.

Picture A

1. Describe what's in the picture.
2. What can you find inside this building?
3. What are the most important museums in your native country?

Picture B

1. Describe what's in the picture.
2. What can you find inside this building?
3. How do movie theaters here differ from movie theaters in your native country?

Pictures A and B

1. Point out those things that are the same and those things that are different in these pictures.
2. Kevin wants to go to the aquarium and his brother Marvin wants to see an adventure movie at the movie theater. Their mother wants to visit the beautiful gardens in the park. The father of the family wants only to spend his day off with his family. What should the family do?

III. Conversation

A.

1. Do you ever read the newspaper?
2. I don't subscribe to one but I always manage to get the Sunday edition.

1. The news always seems to depress me rather than inform me.
2. I always go through the want ads first to see if there are any good jobs available or any interesting cars for sale.

1. I bought a nice camera in the classifieds a few years ago. What section of the newspaper do you read next?
2. I enjoy reading the comics and that's about it.

1. Don't you bother looking at the front page to see what's going on in the world?
2. Oh, I get the news from the TV.

1. I like the news on the radio better. I can work around the house while I'm listening.
2. I don't have a radio but I'm looking for one.

1. There's a big sale at the mall.
2. Oh, thanks but I think I'll check out the want ads first.

B.

1. What do you like to do in your leisure time?
2. I don't like to do anything but my family always pushes me to be active.

1. What sort of things do you like to do?
2. My son likes me to play tennis with him. He's crazy about the sport.

1. I also enjoy a good match on the weekends.
2. My daughter is a movie nut. She wants to study the cinema when she goes to college.

1. I only occasionally like to see a film. I prefer reading.
2. We go to the movies every Sunday. Then we go out to dinner and talk about it.

1. And how about your wife?
2. She loves to go to a museum or if it's a nice day, to go on a picnic in a park or at the beach.

1. You seem to be very busy.
2. Well, that's family life for you.

C.

1. I went to the recreation center over the weekend.
2. Where's that?

1. Every community has one or ought to have one. Ours is on the corner of Second and Main.
2. What did you do there?

1. I played ping-pong, had a lesson in the martial arts, swam, and threw a few games of horseshoes.
2. You really kept busy. Sounds like there's a lot to do.

1. Yes, dancing, crafts, senior citizen get-togethers, just to name a few.
2. Is the center open to everybody?

1. It surely is. Go down there and get their brochure for all the info.
2. Thanks. I think I'll go down there tomorrow. I'm dying for a good swim.

Dialogue Puzzle: With a partner fill in the appropriate responses or questions in the spaces of the dialogue below, then practice and read to the rest of the class.

1. Your brother said you went to the library yesterday.
2. _____

1. Where is it located?
2. _____

1. _____
2. It's easy. Just fill out an application and show some ID and you'll be ready to check out books.

1. _____
2. There are also tapes, records and movies there.

1. That's great. When is it open?
2. _____

1. That's convenient. What kind of books do you like to check out?
2. _____

263

Discussion: Answer the following questions about things talked about in the previous conversations.

1. What kind of books do you like to read for leisure?
2. What's your favorite magazine?
3. What type of museum is very interesting for you?
4. What news was the most important in the past year and how did you hear about it?
5. What's an ideal way to spend a sunny Sunday afternoon?

IV. Reading

A. Vocabulary

journalist	novel	entertainment	editorial
reference	dishes	thesaurus	propose a toast
background	cater to	appreciate	hard-working
struggled	dual	applauded	gathered around

B. Reading

All the students gathered around the table and sang the song that their teacher, Mr. Misuraca, had taught them, "This Land Is Your Land." When they finished, they all applauded and then sat down. The beautiful display of their native dishes smelled incredibly delicious. Gino stood up and proposed a toast, raising his glass and saying, "Welcome here tonight, and since this is our last time together, I just want to say that I hope you find your dreams."

"Just let me learn English, that's all," Chris said, and everyone laughed.

"Well, I have a start," Juan said. "Today I was accepted into a job training program with computers. No more busboy jobs!"

"And good luck to you," Gino said. "That's great. Now let's get to work and start enjoying all this wonderful food from all over the world."

"I'm going back to my native country pretty soon," Maria then said, "but I found out that the English I've learned will help me get a very good job at a hotel that caters to American tourists."

Mohammed then added, "I was a journalist in my native country before the war, and now I hope to write a novel about it and my escape."

"And I hope to read it," Mr. Misuraca said. "You're all doing great, and I want to tell you without using words from a thesaurus that it's been a pleasure teaching you this year. You're hard-working students and I know the English you learned will help you, and you'll succeed at whatever you do. My grandparents came here just like you and they struggled. There were no adult schools so they led a dual life, speaking Italian with each other and forcing their kids to speak only English. They never really enjoyed living in an English-speaking world, and their kids never had the chance to appreciate the beauty of their Italian culture and background."

"But I'm going to stop this editorial and just wish you the best and thanks for being such good students. As Gino said, I hope that you do find your dreams. And don't hesitate to use me as a reference for any future jobs or education."

And they all toasted, ate, sang and had a really good time that night.

C. Exercises

1. Write these sentences in the correct time sequence of the story using a 1 for what came first, all the way to 7 as last.

    _____ a. Gino proposed a toast.

    _____ b. Maria spoke about her job offer in her native country.

    _____ c. All the students sang the song the first time.

    _____ d. Mohammed told about what he wanted to do.

    _____ e. Mr. Misuraca gave his speech.

    _____ f. Juan explained the good news about his job training opportunity.

    _____ g. The students arrived at Gino's house.

2. Write *true* or *false*.

    _____ a. Mr. Misuraca teaches English.

    _____ b. Juan was planning to continue to work as a busboy.

    _____ c. Maria got a job with a hotel in the United States.

    _____ d. Mohammed was a reporter before the war.

    _____ e. Mr. Misuraca's grandparents came from Germany.

    _____ f. Mr. Misuraca's grandparents had a hard time adjusting to life in the United States.

    _____ g. It was a successful party.

3. Vocabulary: Put the vocabulary words from Section A (page 264) in the blank spaces.

    a. The respectable _____ wrote the _____ in the paper.

    b. The restaurant offers many exciting _____ .

    c. They _____ the hero and _____ loudly.

    d. They'll ask you about your educational _____ in the interview.

    e. She leads a _____ life as a waitress and a singer.

    f. When will they _____ , before or after dinner?

    g. Those nightclubs _____ young people.

h. You need at least one _____
   to get that job.
i. Did the audience _____ the
   outstanding _____ ?
j. He looked up the word in the _____ .
k. I read the _____ *Great Expectations* by
   Charles Dickens.
l. The _____ miners _____ to
   earn a decent living.

V. Structure

Review

Exercise S-1:

A. Write the correct form of each verb and its tense in parentheses.

1. (try—Present) He always _____ to attend those concerts.

2. (criticize—Past) _____ Grace _____ your taste in music?

3. (publish—Future) They _____ the book next month.

4. (read/not—Present Continuous) Why _____ you _____ the editorial now?

5. (broadcast—Past Continuous) The TV station _____ the news when the hurricane hit.

6. (change—Future Continuous) They _____ announcers next year.

7. (see/not—Present Perfect) The kids _____ the circus yet.

8. (visit—Present Perfect Continuous) We _____ _____ the botanical gardens for the past hour.

9. (subscribe—Past Perfect) I _____ to the paper before it closed down.

10. (write—Past Perfect Continuous) The author _____ _____ a new novel before he suddenly died.

11. (finish—Future Perfect) He _____ conducting the symphony for the season by the end of November.

Exercise S-2:

B. Change these nouns to adjectives.

1. length _____
2. hope _____
3. excitement _____
4. vision _____
5. commerce _____

6. suspicion _____
7. sorrow _____
8. critic _____
9. introduction _____
10. comic _____

Now write a sentence for each adjective.

1. _____
2. _____
3. _____
4. _____
5. _____
6. _____
7. _____
8. _____
9. _____
10. _____

Exercise S-3:

C. Change these adjectives to nouns.

1. editorial _____
2. busy _____
3. advertising _____
4. classical _____
5. mysterious _____

6. technical _____
7. circulating _____
8. educational _____
9. romantic _____
10. historical _____

Now write a sentence with each noun.

1. _____
2. _____
3. _____
4. _____
5. _____
6. _____
7. _____
8. _____
9. _____
10. _____

Exercise S-4:

D. Write prepositions in the following spaces.

1. _____ dinner he looked _____ the newspaper ads _____ a car _____ buy.

2. She looked _____ the word _____ the dictionary while she was _____ the library.

3. _____ intermission they talked _____ the latest news.

4. He subscribes _____ the newspaper _____ color pictures.

5. The book _____ nuclear disarmament is _____ the shelf _____ the sofa.

Exercise S-5:

E. Connect <u>a</u> clause to the correct <u>b</u> clause.

a.	b.
1. That is the man	if I hadn't been so busy.
2. We wanted to go to the concert	who knows how to sew.
3. I would have gone to the exhibit	he still helped them.
4. She left early	but it was sold out.
5. Although Bob was tired	because she didn't feel well.

Exercise S-6:

F. Correct the punctuation in these sentences.

1. james left new york at 7 o clock

2. he yelled what a surprise

3. where did mr and mrs horton go

VI. Composition

Write your own words in the spaces to make complete sentences.

I _____ like to read. If I want to learn about what's going on in the world, I read _____ . When I'm relaxing or taking it easy, I prefer to read _____ . The most interesting kind of book is _____ . My favorite author is _____ , who is from the country of _____ . I like this writer because _____ _____ . I can read in the languages of _____ .

I think that television is _____ . I watch it _____ . Some of the best programs on TV are _____ . The program that I can't stand is _____ . TV has both its advantages and disadvantages. One of the advantages is _____ while a disadvantage is _____ . I _____ the news on TV.

I enjoy listening to _____ music because _____ . In my native country music is _____ . My favorite musical instrument is _____ . I like how the singer _____ sings because _____ .

I _____ go to the movies. The best kind of movie is _____ because _____ . One of my favorite movies was _____ . I like it because _____ .

VII. Pronunciation

A. First practice these contrasting sounds. Then listen and underline the one word said for each number by the teacher.

1. heat/hit
2. sleep/slip
3. list/least
4. bait/bet
5. sail/sell
6. men/main
7. bad/bed

8. jam/jem
9. than/then
10. stripe/strip
11. hut/hat
12. crush/crash
13. rob/rub
14. calm/come

15. show/chow
16. pull/pool
17. took/talk
18. coal/call
19. flow/flaw
20. fall/foul

B. Listen to the words said and write in the missing letter or letters.

1. __ought
2. __aint
3. __eal
4. __at
5. __ __eet
6. __awn
7. __oke
8. __ound
9. __ail
10. __ __en

11. r __ m
12. f __ ll
13. fl __ at
14. c __ p
15. r __ n
16. d __ ll
17. r __ w
18. sh __ t
19. m __ n
20. b __ ll

21. ba __
22. dea __
23. clo __ __
24. wor __ __
25. ca __ __
26. ro __ __
27. ga __ __
28. mat __
29. win __
30. o __

C. Listen to the sentences dictated and write each correctly.

1. _____
2. _____
3. _____
4. _____
5. _____
6. _____
7. _____
8. _____

A. Newspaper Contents

Births	C2	National News	A3
Bridge	A10	Real Estate	D6
Business	B7	Religion	A12,13
Classified	C2-14	Sports	B1-6
Comics/Crossword	B10	State News	A9
County News	C1	Stock Markets	B7-9
Deaths	C2	Television	D5
Editorials	D2	Travel	D7
Lifestyle	A10,11	Weather	A2
Lively Arts	D4	World News	A4

Exercise L-1: From the newspaper table of contents above, answer these questions.

1. How many sections are in the newspaper? _____

2. Where would you find:

   a. if it'll be sunny or not tomorrow _____

   b. news about local churches _____

   c. who won a baseball game _____

   d. where the movie "Rage" is playing _____

   e. opinions of the newspaper _____

3. What is "Bridge" for? _____

   _____

4. Give examples of World, National, State and County news. ____

   _____

   _____

   _____

   _____

5. Where would you look for something funny? _____

6. What sections would these people look in?

   a. Mr Carson wants to know if his neighbor had her baby yet without disturbing her by phone. _____

   b. Mrs. Hanson wants an inexpensive trip to Peru. _____

   c. Mary is looking for the latest clothes styles. _____

B. Entertainment Guide

MUSEUMS

Museum of Fine Arts—"The Art of Japan," 200 works of paintings, sculpture and prints on display until Jan. 13th, 10 A.M. to 5 P.M. daily except Monday.

Academy of Sciences—Dinosaur exhibit, "How did the dinosaurs die?" plus aquarium and planetarium. Open 11 A.M. to 4:30 P.M., Tuesday thru Saturday.

MUSIC

Piano—Ira Kane plays the music of Beethoven, Jan, 7, 8 P.M. at Sellert Music Hall.

Dixieland Jazz—Friday, Saturday and Sunday, 7:30 P.M. at the Winer Club, performed by the Redhots.

International Folk Songs—At Gaspal College auditorium, Friday, Jan. 14, sung by the New World Choir.

THEATER

Shakespeare's "Hamlet"—performed by the Royal Actors Society at the Lighthouse Theater, weekends at 8 thru the end of the month.

"My Fair Lady"—Musical at Catson Theater, Jan. 7 at 8 P.M.

EVENTS

Flower Show at the Lakeside Garden Center, Sunday, 10 A.M. to 4 P.M. Free.

German Day Festival—Dancing, food, music, children's program, noon to midnight. Memorial Hall.

Health Fair—10 A.M. to 4 P.M. 145 College Ave.

Exercise L-2:

1. When is there a musical playing in this city? _____
   _____

2. Who will play classical music? _____
   _____

3. What's going on at the Academy of Sciences?_____
   _____

4. Jim loves flowers and isn't busy on Sunday. What would you recommend for him to do? _____
   _____

5. Name the band that plays Dixieland jazz. _____

6. Where is "Hamlet" playing and when? _____

7. What is the New World Choir singing? _____

8. What kind of Japanese art is on exhibit at the museum? _____
   _____

C. Card Catalog in the Library

Author Card

```
811        Whitman, Walt 1819-1892
W59614     Leaves of Grass, Introduction by Carl Sandburg.
1921       Modern Library, c1921
           311 p

           I Title
```

Title Card

```
811        Leaves of Grass
W59614     Whitman, Walt 1819-1892
1921       Introduction by Carl Sandburg
           Modern Library, c 1921

           I Title
```

Subject Card

```
811.09     POETS, AMERICAN
W85        Wood, Clement 1888-
           Poets of America, by Clement Wood
           New York, E.P. Dutton and Company, 1925

           I Poets, American
```

Exercise L-3: The cards above are the three ways that cards are filed in the card catalog of the library. If you want to look up a book by a particular author, you look up the _____ card. If you don't know who wrote a book but you remember its title, then you find the _____ card. If you just want to look up a book or books on a particular subject, then you look up the _____ card.

1. John is writing a paper for school about Alaska. He doesn't know anything about it. What card should he look up? _____

   _____

2. Are all three cards above the same book? _____

273

3. Who is the person who wrote *Leaves of Grass*? _____
_____

4. Who is the author of *Poets of America*? _____
_____

5. What is the book by Mr. Wood about? _____

6. Who wrote the introduction to *Leaves of Grass*? _____
_____

7. When are both books published? _____

8. Who are the publishers? _____
_____

9. When did Walt Whitman live? _____

10. How many pages does *Leaves of Grass* have? _____

11. Sue is writing a report on Hollywood. What subject might she look under? _____

IX. Problem Solving

Gary grew up on a farm, and when he was small, his family had many problems. Gary had to drop out of school and help out with the farm. He never learned to read. When he was older his family sold the farm, and he and his wife and new baby moved to the city.

Life was pretty difficult for him because he was not able to read, but he found many ways to "get by." For example, in a restaurant he couldn't read the menu but would always point to a picture or just order something simple, like a hamburger. He wanted to learn to read but it was more important to support his family. His wife helped him a little but he just couldn't learn from her. Also, now he felt bad that his daughter would soon grow up and want bedtime stories read to her. He got a job in a factory that required little reading. One day the boss offered him a promotion. However, he knew the job required reading.

A. What is the problem? _____
_____
_____
_____

B. What are the solutions? _____
_____
_____
_____

C. Which is the best solution? _____
_____
_____
_____

274

Answer Key

UNIT 1—Shopping

IV. Reading (page 17)

C. Exercises

1. a. She writes to her mother every Tuesday afternoon.
    b. A blank piece of paper is on her desk.
    c. She's thinking of what to write.
    d. No. There aren't enough products there, and the food isn't fresh.
    e. The mannequins and the escalators fascinate him.
    f. People bargain for used items.
    g. Yes, they are very popular.

2. a. T   e. T
    b. T   f. F
    c. F   g. T
    d. T

3. a. consumer/aware
    b. stationery/similar
    c. executive/sip
    d. timid/behaves
    e. variety/experiences/impressions
    f. mannequin/stares
    g. jokes/a little while
    h. correspondence
    i. reasonable/bargain
    j. branch
    k. items

V. Structure (page 19)

Nouns

Ex. S-1

1. The <u>consumer</u> always recycles his aluminum <u>cans</u>.

    s   o
2. The mysterious <u>credit card</u> is creating too much <u>confusion</u>.

               s   o
3. <u>Henry</u> is buying a new <u>refrigerator</u> now.

 s   o
4. <u>Advertising</u> sometimes deceives <u>consumers</u>.

  s   o

Plurals

Ex. S-2

1. dresses
2. shelves
3. bays
4. mice
5. accounts
6. pianos
7. salesmen
8. crises
9. warranties
10. heroes
11. oxen
12. sisters-in-law
13. boxes
14. peaches
15. teeth
16. potatoes
17. lives
18. fish

Collective Nouns

Ex. S-3

1. plays   2. are   3. is

Count and Non-Count Nouns

Ex. S-4

1. much
2. few
3. some
4. many
5. little
6. some
7. many
8. little
9. Many
10. some
11. is/much
12. are/few

Possessive Nouns

Ex. S-5

1. the store's owner
2. the women's decision
3. those stores' parking lot
4. your cousin's store's sale

Suffix

Ex. S-6

1. sadness
2. reflection
3. excitement
4. clearance
5. conference
6. pressure
7. heroism
8. ability
9. missionary, bakery, inventory
10. fortitude

Ex. S-7

ness = nervousness
ism = tourism
ure = departure
ity = authority
tude = solitude
ory = depository

1. departure
2. tourism
3. nervousness
4. depository
5. solitude
6. authority

Ex. S-8

1. attendance
2. excitement
3. investigation
4. dependence
5. improvement
6. intention
7. difference
8. entrance

Present and Present Continuous Verbs

(Present Continuous is also known as the Present Progressive.)

Ex. S-10

1. Do/receive/receive
2. Does/read/doesn't/read
3. Do/check/do
4. does/pay/pays
5. do/buy/buy
6. Does/understand/doesn't
7. Does/tax/taxes

Ex. S-11

1. Is/planning/isn't planning
2. Are/thinking/I am
3. Are/taking/are taking
4. Are/handing/they aren't
5. Are/going/are checking
6. Is/trying/isn't trying
7. Is/showing/is showing

VIII. Life Skills (page 28)

A. Clothing Labels

Ex. L-1

1. Wash by hand, not in the washing machine, and hang to dry, not in the dryer.
2. Just clean with a damp cloth. Don't wash in the washing machine.
3. He shouldn't use the regular cycle of the washing machine or use strong detergent or bleach. He shouldn't twist, ring or tumble dry high.
4. SANA/SPORTS CLUB/SPORTS CLUB AND SANA/MASON'S
5. His white undershirts turn pink.
6. Permanent Press

B. Department Store Directory

Ex. L-2

1. Cosmetics/3rd
2. Furniture/4th
3. Linen/2nd
4. Kitchenware/lower level
5. Toys/3rd
6. Offices/2nd
7. That's in the stationery on the 1st floor.
8. They're in children's on the 4th floor.
9. That's in personnel on the 2nd floor.
10. Those are in appliances on the lower level.
11. That's in books on the 1st floor.
12. They're in shoes on the 1st floor.
13. Where can I find dresses? (blouses, etc.)
14. Do you know where VCRs are? (TVs, radios, etc.)
15. Where are men's suits? (pants, shirts, etc.)

C. Comparison Shopping

Ex. L-3

1. Until the 15th of the month.
2. You save $50 on the JZR 13″ TV, and $94 on the Langer 19″ TV.
3. The JZR TV is 13 inches with remote control while the Langer is 19 inches with regular control.
4. It doesn't offer the sale in Concord.
5. It means to buy on credit, the same amount each month, but paying more in total.

D. Warranties

Ex. L-4

1. The warranty is good for 1 year.
2. No. To drop it is not "normal" consumer use.
3. You need a receipt or other proof of date of purchase.
4. Yes. Most reputable companies offer warranties on their products.

IV. Reading (page 38)

C. Exercises

1. a. 4
    b. 7
    c. 1
    d. 5
    e. 6
    f. 3
    g. 2

2. a. T
    b. T
    c. F
    d. T
    e. F
    f. F

3. a. chop
    b. groceries
    c. hum
    d. grate
    e. go through
    f. total up
    g. bargains
    h. ingredients
    i. embarrassed
    j. relieved
    k. items remaining
    l. aisle
    m. checkout counter
    n. realize
    o. dish

V. Structure (page 40)

Personal Pronouns

Ex. S-1

She/them/she/it/She/it/it

Ex. S-2

a. my, yours
b. Our, theirs
c. yours
d. her, your

Ex. S-3

a. myself
b. yourself
c. himself
d. themselves

Review Ex. S-4

his/it/He/his/their/they/her/I/I
I/you/yourself/His/his/your/mine/I

Review Ex. S-5

his/their/their/It/they/himself/They
it/I/you/we/me/him/you/she/him
his/it/her

B. Indefinite Pronouns

Ex. S-6

1. any(thing)
2. some
3. anyone

Ex. S-7

1. No one
2. None
3. nothing
4. Neither

Ex. S-8

1. everyone/all
2. Both/each other
3. Few/everybody
4. another/more
5. Either
6. One another/Several/
   others

Ex. S-9

1. b
2. a
3. c
4. a
5. b
6. c
7. a
8. c
9. b
10. b
11. a

Past and Continuous Verbs

Ex. S-10

1. Did/marinate/marinated
2. Did/spoil/it didn't
3. did/sift/sifted
4. Did/bring/brought
5. Did/stuff/stuffed
6. did/need/needed/didn't need
7. did/beat/beat
8. Did/stick/it did
9. Did/take/he/she did
10. checked/she did

Ex. S-11

1. cutting/were cutting
2. Was/munching/he was
3. was/helping/was helping
4. was/dragging/wasn't eating
5. Was/totaling up/he wasn't/He was stacking
6. Was/writing/was writing

Ex. S-12

1. arrived/was cooking
2. were boiling/read
3. was sleeping/called
4. were steaming/rang

VIII. Life Skills (page 49)

A. Supermarket Shopping List

Ex. L-1

1. butter
   swiss cheese
   yogurt

2. ginger ale
   diet cola
   mineral water

3. carrots
   cantaloupe
   lettuce

4. egg noodles
   rice
   spaghetti

5. mouthwash
   deodorant
   toothpaste

6. cornflakes
   brown sugar
   oatmeal

7. rubber gloves
   furniture polish
   air freshener

8. olives
   chunk light tuna
   can of pinto beans

9. oregano
   salad dressing
   vegetable oil

10. TV dinner
    frozen orange juice
    frozen vegetables

11. fresh shrimp
    pork chops
    ground chuck

12. marmalade
    cranberry juice
    peanut butter

13. rolls
    cake
    whole wheat bread

14. toilet paper
    tissues
    napkins

15. jellybeans
    fig bar cookies
    saltine crackers

B. Food Labels

Ex. L-2

1. You should add water or milk.
2. No. It has sodium.
3. Yes, it has 2¾ servings.
4. The soup has fewer calories, 90 with water and 160 with milk.
5. Yes. It has 40% of the US RDA.
6. It's the weight of the food only. This soup weighs 10¾ ounces.
7. Zesty-O soup costs less per ounce.
8. Store it in the refrigerator after you open it.
   Keep it in the freezer until ready to use.
   Put one egg into the mixture when preparing.
   After this date the product isn't guaranteed to be good.
   This is fresh food that might spoil quickly without refrigeration.

C. Comparative Shopping

Ex. L-3

1. One is $1.89 and is ground chuck while the other is $ .98 and is ground beef. The ground chuck is better quality.
2. Softie napkins are cheaper. (.79/140 = .56¢ per napkin; $1.89/360 = .53¢ per napkin).
3. Bob's has the better deal. Apples there are 25¢ per pound, compared to 39¢ at Sunset.
4. Bob's is 10 cents more.
5. Mertson's ($1.39/32 = .043) is less than El Mar ($1.99/44 = .045).
6. Bell tuna at Bob's is 10 cents cheaper. Captain John's tuna at Sunset market comes in either water or oil.
7.

2 lbs. apples	$ .50
4 cans tuna	2.36
(4 x 59)	
5 lbs chuck	9.45
(5 x 1.89)	
	————
	$12.31

$20.00
−12.31
————
$ 7.69

You would get $7.69 in change.

8.

SUNSET		BOB'S
$1.99	catsup	$1.39
1.49	sugar	1.39
2.07	tuna	1.77
(3x69)		(3x59)
————		————
$5.55		$4.75

Jose had the smaller bill at Bob's market.

D. Recipes

Ex. L-4

1. 1 tablespoon of sugar/3 teaspoons of baking powder/½ teaspoon of salt/2 tablespoons salad oil
2. Sift them together.
3. Add them to the dry ingredients.
4. 1¼ cups of flour/1 cup of milk
5. You bake them on a hot griddle.
6. There are 4 people and the recipe makes 6 average-sized pancakes. Maybe more are needed.
7. Optional answer

E. Menu

Ex. L-5

1. It's open from 5 to 10 P.M. Yes, he could stop there on Tuesday night at 8:30.
2. "I'm sorry but we don't serve wine."
3.

Henry	Margaret
$1.35	$ 1.75
7.95	.75
.80	10.95
.40	.40
$10.50	$13.85

Margaret had the higher bill.

4. A la carte is just the entree. Dinner is the entree plus soup or salad, vegetables, bread, rice or potato and dessert.
5. "The minimum service is $2.50. What else would you like?"
6. A prime rib or prawns dinner is the most expensive item.
7. Ask the waitress.
8. Because she ate too much and now feels that by eating only salad, she'll lose any extra weight.
9. No, it isn't. The waitress charged for a prime rib dinner when actually it was a la carte. The bill should be 3 dollars cheaper, at $30.10.

The tip answers should vary.

UNIT 3—Health

IV. Reading (page 62)

C. Exercises

1.
a. 5
b. 7
c. 2
d. 4
e. 1
f. 6
g. 3

2.
a. T
b. F
c. F
d. T
e. T
f. F
g. T

3.
a. Chicken pox
b. get in touch with
c. do business
d. prone
e. surgical
f. annual/pass out
g. are supposed to
h. relieved/ misunderstand
i. arrange
j. get the chance/ take in the sights
k. particular
l. ambulance
m. panic

V. Structure (page 64)

Subject and Verb Agreement

Ex. S-1

1. is
2. seems
3. meets
4. knows
5. is
6. has
7. is
8. were
9. am
10. are
11. are
12. has
13. deserve
14. is
15. is
16. was
17. is
18. wants
19. arrives
20. has

Future Continuous

Ex. S-2

1. Will/keep/will keep
2. Is/going to sprain/is going to sprain
3. Will/bill/won't bill
4. Is/going to complain/is not going to complain
5. Will/operate/he/she will
6. Is/going to catch/she is
7. Will/faint/she won't
8. Is/going to keep/is going to keep
9. Will/take care/will
10. Is/going to borrow/am going to borrow

Ex. S-3

1. Will/be taking care of/will be taking care of
2. Will/be suffering/won't be suffering
3. Will/be dealing/won't
4. Will/be taking/will
5. Will/be helping/will be helping
6. Are/going to be talking/am going to be talking

VIII. Life Skills (page 71)

A. Immunizations

Ex. L-1

1. Seven
2. Polio
3. Measles, mumps and rubella
4. Four
5. After 1 year old
6. Because they must be given at certain age intervals of the child's growth, 2 months, 4, 6, and 18.
7. As science gains new knowledge
8. A school

B. Health Services

Ex. L-3

1. Alcohol Abuse Center
2. Drug Abuse Center
3. Children's Health Services
4. Crisis or Family Counseling
5. Suicide Prevention
6. Optional

E. Medicine Labels

Ex. L-6

1. Any drugstore. Anyone.
2. Six
3. Yes
4. Coughing and nasal stuffiness
5. Henry Smith
6. Yes
7. 560 Trail Blvd., Marat, NY
8. 8 P.M.
9. No
10. San Mateo Medical Center

Ex. L-7

1. Over the counter
2. Avoid spraying in eyes, mouth, ears or other sensitive areas of the body.
3. All three

IV. Reading (page 83)

C. Exercises

1.	a. 3	2.	a. F
	b. 4		b. T
	c. 1		c. F
	d. 7		d. T
	e. 5		e. F
	f. 6		f. T
	g. 2		g. T

3.
  a. dial
  b. hang up/receiver
  c. chip in
  d. in person
  e. motioned/
     couldn't take it
  f. over

  g. signal/steep
  h. giggle
  i. get off/get through
     long distance
  j. put down
  k. convince

V. Structure (page 85)

Comparison of Adjectives

Ex. S-2

1. louder   2. more expensive   3. easier

Ex. S-3

1. brightest   2. most complicated   3. busiest

Ex. S-4

1. flatter/flattest
2. wiser/wisest
3. prettier/prettiest
4. earlier/earliest
5. more brilliant/most brilliant
6. more thoughtful/most thoughtful
7. more slippery/most slippery
8. more amazing/most amazing
9. worse/worst
10. more tired or tireder/most tired or tiredest

Ex. S-6

1. best
2. cheaper
3. more serious
4. most careful
5. sleepier

6. nicer
7. thinnest
8. more reliable
9. bad
10. less

Suffixes

1. mysterious
2. informative
3. stylish
4. gradual
5. agreeable

6. horrible
7. doubtful
8. homeless
9. faulty
10. tragic

Ex. S-7

1. oily
2. joyous
3. inquisitive
4. practical
5. careless

6. wonderful
7. foolish
8. responsible
9. lovable

1. practical
2. foolish
3. inquisitive, wonderful
4. joyous

5. careless
6. responsible
7. oily
8. lovable

Ex. S-8

1. humorous
2. forgetful
3. disastrous
4. cheerful

5. courteous
6. washable
7. successful
8. preferable

Helping Verbs—may/might

Ex. S-10

1. She may have the report ready by noon.
2. Mr. Carson may give them an exam.
3. You may use the phone.
4. She might have woken up.
5. He might have drowned.

VIII. Life Skills (page 97)

A. Pay Telephone

1. 20 cents
2. No
3. Listen for the tone.
4. Call 800-621-0430
5. 0 + Area Code + Number
6. Dial 411 and get assistance.
7. 00
8. In the slot below where it says "Push for Coin."

B. White Pages

1. You find all the telephone listings.
2. 985 and 986
3. First name. His address.
4. The white or yellow pages. Dial 911.
5. Helpful community information.
6. Call the Armenian Cultural Center.
7. People move and their phone numbers change. New phones are installed.
8. The yellow pages.
9. 986-7234

D. Telephone Messages

DATE: July 16th
TIME: 1:30 P.M.
FOR: Mr. Kane
FROM: Kitty Carson of Hoffmin's Plastics
PLEASE CALL BACK
MESSAGE: They're ready to bring over the supplies you ordered. A delivery person will be there tomorrow at 9 A.M. if that's OK with you. Leave a message with her secretary.

E. Long Distance Rates

1. $2.84
2. $4.10
3. Direct Distance Dialed—Station to Station
   All days 11 A.M.—8 A.M.
   Sat. 8 A.M.—11 P.M.
   Sun. 8 A.M.—5 P.M.
4. Operator assisted.
   All days and hours.
5. ($3.23)
6. $11.25 (Alice's call)
   -3.04 (Your call)
   —————
   $ 8.21 (difference)

UNIT 5—Emergencies

IV. Reading (page 106)

C. Exercises

1. a. 3
   b. 6
   c. 1
   d. 4
   e. 7
   f. 5
   g. 2

2. a. F
   b. T
   c. F
   d. F
   e. T
   f. T
   g. T

3. a. in the nick of time
   b. shock/live wire
   c. chemicals
   d. harmful/household
   e. prevent
   f. scared
   g. food poisoning
   h. hurricane/approach
   i. set ____ on fire
   j. Either/potluck/or
   k. poison ivy
   l. tripped

285

V. Structure (page 108)

Articles

Ex. S-1

1. The/a
2. the/the/a/a/the
3. the/the
4. An/the

Ex. S-2

1. the/the/___/___/___
2. the/a/___
3. a/the/the
4. The/___/the
5. The/___
6. ___/a
7. ___
8. the
9. ___/___/the
10. ___/the

Ex. S-3

a/a/The/the/an/___/___/the/___/the/the/a/the/the

Infinitives

Ex. S-4

1. to take
2. to press
3. to wreck

Gerunds

Ex. S-5

1. keeping
2. being
3. buying
4. Practicing

Ex. S-7

1. A. talking / B. Mrs. Cook hates to talk about disasters.
2. A. bleeding / B. My cousin started to bleed right after she cut herself.
3. A. helping / B. They like to help others.
4. A. using / B. The company will begin to use safety packaging.
5. A. going / B. She loves to go shopping.
6. A. informing / B. The business neglected to inform the authorities of the gas leak.

Ex. S-9

1. The paramedic stopped . . .
      giving CPR,
      taking his pulse, etc.
2. The policeman talked about . . .
      saying no to drugs,
      working late at night in the city, etc.
3. The fireman enjoyed . . .
      saving people,
      putting out fires, etc.

VIII. Life Skills (page 115)

B. First Aid
1. Put cold water or wet towels on his burn, and then cover with a clean cloth.
2. "Don't break it. See a doctor first."
3. She should call for help or a hospital, and then cover herself with a blanket and raise her legs.
4. Call emergency and flush his face with water until help arrives.

C. Disaster
1. At a Red Cross disaster service center.
2. Food, clothing, medical care, rent for a place to stay until their home can be repaired or rebuilt.
3. It isn't necessary for the family to take anything with them. They should wear clothing appropriate for the season.
4. Optional

UNIT 6—Jobs

IV. Reading (page 123)

C. Exercises

1.
   a. 4
   b. 7
   c. 1
   d. 6
   e. 3
   f. 2
   g. 5

2.
   a. T
   b. F
   c. T
   d. T
   e. F
   f. T
   g. T

3.
   a. write down/schedule
   b. made fun of
   c. bulletin board
   d. filled out/
   right there on the spot
   e. at least
   f. exhausted/dropped
   g. career/In the
   meantime
   h. start out/shift
   i. hire/benefits
   j. minimum

V. Structure (page 125)

Adverbs

Ex. S-1
1. tomorrow
2. too
3. completely
4. only slightly
5. carefully
6. soon
7. seldom

Ex. S-2
1. rapidly
2. easily
3. hopefully
4. truly
5. clearly
6. automatically
7. terribly
8. daily
9. suitably
10. scientifically

Ex. S-4

1. slow
2. well
3. carelessly
4. impressive
5. good
6. attentively
7. correct
8. angry
9. quickly
10. delicious

Ex. S-6

1. more respectfully
2. more carefully
3. most neatly
4. more slowly
5. most quietly

Ex. S-7

1. still
2. anymore
3. anymore
4. still
5. still

Ex. S-8

1. ... the teller did ...
   The manager arrived late and the teller did also.
   The manager arrived late and so did the teller.
2. My brother can speak English and my niece can too.
   My brother can speak English and my niece can also.
   My brother can speak English and so can my niece.
3. Bob is studying in a job training program and Mary is too.
   Bob is studying in a job training program and Mary is also.
   Bob is studying in a job training program and so is Mary.
4. Mr. Mack got his paycheck on Friday and Mr. Johnson did too.
   Mr. Mack got his paycheck on Friday and Mr. Johnson did also.
   Mr. Mack got his paycheck on Friday and so did Mr. Johnson.

Ex. S-9

1. ... her friend shouldn't ...
   She shouldn't work there ... should her friend.
2. Bob wouldn't say that and Mary wouldn't either.
   Bob wouldn't say that and neither would Mary.
3. I didn't apply for that job and my neighbor didn't either.
   I didn't apply for that job and neither did my neighbor.

Present Perfect and Present Perfect Continuous

Ex. S-10

1. Have/filled
2. has left
3. has/returned
4. hasn't worked
5. has cared for/helped
6. have studied
7. Has/forgotten/she has
8. haven't understood

Ex. S-14

1. lived
2. have lived
3. worked
4. has worked
5. studied
6. has studied
7. has/finished
8. finished
9. left/has lived
10. has spoken

Ex. S-15

1. has been waiting
2. has been talking
3. Have/been arguing
4. hasn't been studying
5. Has/been raining/ it hasn't
6. have been expecting
7. Has/been planning/ he has
8. hasn't been taking

VIII. Life Skills (page 136)

A. Classified Ads

1.
<u>Telephone</u> <u>Call</u>	<u>Letter</u>	<u>In Person</u>
Apt. Manager	Accountant	Dishwasher
Grill Cook	Teacher	Sales
Dental Receptionist		
Haircutters		
Nursing Assistants		

2. Apt. manager, dishwasher, sales
3. Accountant, haircutter, teacher
4. Baker's Department Store. They don't discriminate.
5. Yes. The work is for breakfast and lunch.
6. Rent reduction. Light or easy duties.
7. Accountant and teacher.
8. Haircutter and teacher.
9. Dental receptionist and haircutter.
10. No. They ask for "mature" and she's only 18. Also they prefer experience.

B. Qualifications

1. e
2. c
3. b
4. f
5. d
6. h
7. a
8. g

C. Work Duties

1. c
2. f
3. b
4. h
5. a
6. d
7. e
8. g

E. Interview

1. Y
2. Y
3. Y
4. N
5. Y
6. N
7. N
8. N
9. Y
10. N
11. Y
12. Y
13. N
14. Y
15. N
16. Y
17. N
18. N
19. N
20. Y
21. Y
22. Perhaps not aggressive, but indicate strong interest
23. N

UNIT 7—Banking

I. Vocabulary (page 145)

Ex. V-I

cash—line—teller—window—currency—coins—
account—deposit—withdraw
interest—brochure—bill—checking—minimum—
service—safe deposit
money—drive up window—mail—automatic teller—
bank—quarterly—annual—overdraw—check—
endorse—loan—establish credit

IV. Reading (page 149)

C. Exercises

1. a. 6
   b. 7
   c. 2
   d. 3
   e. 1
   f. 4
   g. 5

2. a. F
   b. T
   c. F
   d. T
   e. T
   f. F
   g. F

3. a. shrugged/confused
   b. get
   c. got out of
   d. recommend
   e. reward
   f. loading zone
   g. drives off/windshield
   h. takes care of/errands
   i. Instead/procedures
      pass the time
   j. yell/competent

V. Structure (page 151)

Prepositions (Other answers are possible.)

Ex. S-1

1. aboard
2. across (in)
3. against
4. among
5. of
6. at (with)
7. under (beneath)
8. above
9. beyond
10. besides (with)
11. down (along/on)
12. by (at)
13. by
14. from
15. for
16. in
17. of
18. off
19. on/at
20. on/beyond/for
21. over
22. across
23. throughout (across)
24. until
25. below
26. per
27. During/in
28. on/of/on/with
29. without/to
30. Outside/Inside

Participles

Ex. S-3

1. exciting
2. disturbing
3. Smiling/whistling
4. working
5. talking
6. interesting

290

Ex. S-4

1. endorsed
2. vanished
3. arrived
4. addressed

5. Watered/given
6. balanced
7. known

VIII. Life Skills (page 161)

A. Checks

DATE

JACKSON'S $61.87

SIXTY-ONE AND 87/100_____

SIGNATURE

DATE

STAR TELEPHONE $134.55

ONE HUNDRED AND THIRTY-FOUR AND 55/100_____

SIGNATURE

DATE

KATHY RILEY $20.00

TWENTY AND 00/100_____

SIGNATURE

277	JACKSON'S	61.87	938.13
278	STAR TELEPHONE	134.55	803.58
279	KATHY RILEY	20.00	783.58

B. Bank Forms

Date

	11-35	$65.37
	90-1936	30.00
	Total	95.37
	Less cash	25.00
	Net	70.37

Signature

Date

798-1 2 3265465

$300.00

THREE HUNDRED

Signature

Address

C. Credit Cards

Ex. L-1

1. Maria Gibson
2. 3/89
3. 743 349 685 98 01
4. Call TISA emergency number for lost cards

Ex. L-2

1. $486.32
2. 11-24-89
3. No, she can pay 25 dollars and pay the rest later with interest.
4. 18%

UNIT 8—Housing

IV. Reading (page 170)

C. Exercises

1.
   a. 3
   b. 6
   c. 2
   d. 1
   e. 5
   f. 4
   g. 7

2.
   a. T
   b. F
   c. F
   d. F
   e. T
   f. T
   g. T

3.
   a. bit
   b. furnished
   c. facilities
   d. inconvenient
   e. condominium
   f. utilities
   g. can't stand
   h. swinging bachelor
   i. get in the way
   j. arrangement
   k. split/ways
   l. realtor/environment
   m. practical

V. Structure (page 172)

Prepositional Phrases

Ex. S-1

1. on account of
2. regardless of
3. out of respect for
4. in addition to

B. Two Word Verbs

Ex. S-2

1. surprised at
2. paid for
3. suffered from
4. apologize for
5. succeeded in
6. agrees with
7. cares for
8. explained/to
9. apply for
10. asked for

Past Perfect

Ex. S-3

1. had talked
2. had taken
3. had caught
4. had arrived
5. hadn't heard

6. Had ____ been
7. had rented
8. had signed
9. had ____ had
10. Had ____ known

Ex. S-6

1. had been talking
2. had been waiting

3. had been discussing
4. had been cleaning

VIII. Life Skills (page 179)

A. Classified Ads

Ex. L-1

1. 678-5434
2. Unfurnished Duplexes (2 houses together) or Triplexes (3 houses)
3. 678-5434, 645-3331
4. 688-5678
5. Pool, sauna, and security
6. Furn = furnished, frwy = freeway, beaut = beautiful, BR = bedroom, BA = bathroom, lr = large, kitch = kitchen, w/ = with, w/w = wall to wall, drps = drapes, encl = enclosed, gar = garage, frplcs = fireplaces, micro = microwave oven, bldg = building, decor = decorated, AEK = all electric kitchen, nr = near, trans = transportation, immac = immaculate, dep = deposit, sec = security, fam. rm. = family room, mo = month, incl = included
7. Wells duplex
8. Wells 4 bedroom house (unfurnished)
9. To attract people who like to enjoy a fireplace in their house.
10. a) What kind of stove is it? Is there a deposit? What color are the carpets? etc.
    b) How big is the yard? Where is it located? How much is it to buy? etc.

Ex. L-2

1. For tenants or landlords who have problems with rental housing.
2. Human Relations Division
3. Optional answer
4. There is a fair judgment.
5. To reduce problems that often the court system has to deal with.

Ex. L-3

1. The small section to the right of the dotted line.
2. 12/15/88 to 2/16/89
3. Bob Brown/$37.25/water and sewer
4. Within 20 days after the date on which it is billed (3/12/86).
5. Service will be discontinued.
6. $10
7. Optional answer
8. Optional answer

UNIT 9—Transportation

IV. Reading (page 190)

C. Exercises

1. a. 6
   b. 3
   c. 4
   d. 1
   e. 7
   f. 5
   g. 2

2. a. T
   b. F
   c. F
   d. F
   e. T
   f. T
   g. T

3. a. went dead
   b. mechanic/worth a try
   c. turn over/blew his top
   d. have a look/upcoming
   e. stuck
   f. drive off
   g. On our way/intersection
   h. ignition
   i. hood
   j. dejectedly
   k. lemon

V. Structure (page 192)

Conjunctions

Ex. S-1

1. but
2. and
3. or

Ex. S-2

1. both . . . and
2. not only . . . but also
3. as . . . as
4. whether . . . or
5. either . . . or
6. so . . . that
7. as . . . as
8. such . . . that
9. neither . . . nor

Future Perfect

Ex. S-3

1. will have finished
2. will have changed
3. will have cleaned
4. will have taken
5. will have/set
6. will not have forgotten
7. will/have been
8. will have become
9. will have understood
10. will have flown

VIII. Life Skills (page 197)

A. Road Signs

Ex. L-1

1. You see it where a small road leads to a large road.
   A two lane road will become four, two on each side that allows for easier passing of slow traffic.
2. You see it where a large highway ends and becomes two lanes.
   Be ready to slow down and drive carefully when passing other cars.
3. You see it where one road leads into another.
   Let other traffic pass first.

4. You see it at an intersection.
   Don't turn right. It's probably a one way street.
5. You see it at an intersection.
   Don't turn around on this street.
6. You see it on a freeway or highway in the country.
   Be careful of deer running across the road.
7. You see it on a road.
   Be careful of slipping or skidding when you turn or brake in the rain.
8. You see it in the street.
   Watch out for people crossing the road in a crosswalk.
9. You see it just before a bridge, a tunnel or some other structure with a roof.
   Be careful if you have a truck or high vehicle.
10. You see it on a highway.
    Keep to the right side.
11. You see it on a street or road.
    Don't go into it. It's probably a one-way street.
12. You see it on a street or road.
    Don't drive a truck here.
13. You see it on a street or road.
    Be prepared to stop for a traffic signal.
14. You see it where one road meets or joins another.
    Be careful of cars driving in the same lane.
15. You see it on a two-lane highway.
    Be careful when passing slower traffic.
16. You see it on a street by a school.
    Be careful of children crossing the street.
17. You see it on a highway.
    Be prepared to go up or down. Be careful of slow or fast trucks.
18. You see it on a two-lane highway.
    Don't pass slower traffic.

B. Car Repair

Ex. L-2

1. There was a strange sound when she applied the brakes.
2. $30 for labor.
3. Karen Lee. Ford Granada. 4:30 P.M.
4. Yes. By phone.
5. $32.85/$60.00/$92.85
6. Yes, she was given an estimate and then asked to approve the revised estimate.

C. Driver's License

Ex. L-3

1. Yes, in #1, a physical impairment.
2. #2 Yes. #3 Yes. Drunk Driving, Olympic Courthouse, March 3rd.
3. #4 State: Virginia/License No. 342 JHL

D. Car Ads

Ex. L-4

1. auto = automatic transmission
   ps = power steering
   pb = power brakes
   air = air conditioning
   loaded = It has many features.

E. Bus Schedule

Ex. L-5

1. 43C
2. Elm
3. Yes
4. No/Yes
5. Every 15 minutes.

UNIT 10—Education

IV. Reading (page 208)

C. Exercises

1.
a. 3
b. 1
c. 4
d. 5
e. 2
f. 6
g. 7

2.
a. T
b. F
c. T
d. T
e. T
f. T
g. F

3.
a. honor/scholarship
b. reluctantly/homework
c. find the time
d. support/community
e. veterinarian
f. get out of
g. remind/attend/conference
h. grade
i. a taste of his own medicine

V. Structure (page 210)

Conjunctions

Ex. S-1

1. Although
2. because
3. unless
4. than
5. so that
6. While
7. When
8. before
9. so that
10. until

Conditional

Ex. S-2

1. will meet
2. gives
3. will show up
4. have
5. doesn't speak

Ex. S-3

1. would be
2. would speak
3. knew
4. wouldn't buy
5. had

Ex. S-4

1. would have given
2. had been
3. had gotten
4. had notified
5. had done

Ex. S-5

1. would come
2. will meet
3. wouldn't have visited
4. doesn't have
5. had told
6. tried

VIII. Life Skills (page 219)

Ex. L-1

1. On the answer sheet
2. Fill in the correct circle, a, b, c or d on the answer sheet.
3. No. Pencil only.
4. No, only one.
5. Carefully, keeping in mind that you have 40 minutes.
6. The teacher will say when there are five minutes left.
7. No, he should erase the first mark.
8. No, she should have done the computation on a piece of scratch paper.
9. He marked two answer keys.

UNIT 11—Law

IV. Reading (page 228)

C. Exercises

1.
   a. 1
   b. 4
   c. 2
   d. 5
   e. 3
   f. 7
   g. 6

2.
   a. T
   b. F
   c. T
   d. F
   e. T
   f. F
   g. F

3.
   a. go on
   b. hurriedly/city hall
   c. witness/testify
   d. mugger
   e. tripped
   f. damages
   g. fiancee/pedestrian
   h. out front/loading zone
   i. work out
   j. requirements
   k. snap
   l. cable

V. Structure (page 230)

Relative Clauses

Ex. S-1

1. that
2. who (that)
3. who (that)
4. whom
5. that

Ex. S-2

1. Do you want to hire a lawyer who specializes in child support?
2. The man who lost $5000 in the robbery is moving to Texas.
3. Everyone who (that) has met him seems to like him.
4. Bob talked to a policeman who (that) explained the Miranda advice.
5. Where are the papers that you ordered?
6. Is that the divorce lawyer whom (that) your neighbor hired?
7. The office that I used to have was much bigger than this.
8. I met the student whom (that) she told me about.

Ex. S-3

1. The law office whose secretaries are bilingual is moving.
2. Do you know the bailiff whose responsibility is to keep order in the court?

Ex. S-4

1. His sister, who is in college, speaks three languages.
2. His uncle, who lives in Denver, is his mother's brother.
3. (No commas)
4. Mrs. Hogan, who worked as a bookkeeper before, is the new receptionist.
5. (No commas)
6. Jasper Electronics, which is located near the freeway, has an excellent reputation for well-made products.

Wish Verbs

Ex. S-5

1. were	6. could visit
2. could	7. had had
3. had	8. had studied
4. hadn't rained	9. hadn't committed
5. had been	10. lived

Ex. S-6

1. I wish you would help me carry these suitcases.
2. I wish you wouldn't make any errors.
3. I wish you would take this message.

Ex. S-7

1. wishes/could go
2. hope/will be able

VIII. Life Skills (page 237)

A. Legal Advice

Ex. L-1

1. a. x
   b. __
   c. x
   d. __
   e. __
   f. x
   g. x
   h. __
   i. x
   j. __
   k. x
2. d, e, a, c, f

B. Traffic Violations

Ex. L-2

1. A child didn't have a restraint device in a car.
2. $52. Nothing.
3. From a law enforcement officer.
4. Disregard the notice.
5. July 16, 1988.
6. Cash

D. City Ordinances

Ex. L-3

1. On a sidewalk in the city.
2. Mostly kids.
3. Somebody probably got hit or almost hit.
4. Maybe they don't have many kids.

E. Contracts

Ex. L-4

a. 3
b. 1
c. 2
d. 4

UNIT 12—Post Office

IV. Reading (page 245)

C. Exercises

1.		2.		3.			
a.	6	a.	F	a.	valuables	g.	smiles from ear to ear/
b.	7	b.	T	b.	awful/concerning		authentic
c.	2	c.	T	c.	uneasy	h.	post office box
d.	4	d.	F	d.	glance/bulletin board	i.	midst/fraud
e.	7	e.	F	e.	accused/zone	j.	out loud
f.	3	f.	F	f.	exchange		
g.	1	g.	F				

V. Structure (page 247)

Punctuation

Ex. S-1

1. The freeway between San Francisco and San Jose is long, straight, and sometimes boring.
2. Bob Johnson, our dentist, lives at 345 Elm St., Smallville, Ohio.

3.
January 7, 1987

Dear sirs:

I'm writing this letter to complain about the service we received at your store in Miami. John Quinn, the salesman, treated us very badly, and the merchandise we bought was defective. I hope this doesn't happen again.

Sincerely,

Don Smith

4. Bob asked, "How much is it to send a registered letter?"
5. Since you asked, I'll explain it to you.
6. Gee! That was close!
7. His sister-in-law is very self-centered.
8. Bob's friend isn't going to New York.
9. I enjoyed reading the article "The Joy of Cooking" in that magazine.
10. The problem—that I was talking about last week—really hasn't gotten any better.

VIII. Life Skills (page 253)

A. Money Orders

Ex. L-1

1. $25.00
2. Zack Hearst
3. John Miller for yard work
4. The amount. (Not more than that)
   Don't stamp, write or mark above the line.
   Who gets it.
   Who purchased it.
   The number.
5. John Miller
6. 60 days
7. Present receipt and file a claim for refund at the post office.

B. Change of Address

Ex. L-2

1. Not more than a year.

2. X Individual Signer Only

   75 Alpine Dr.
   Apt. 4
   Burlingame, CA 94010

   Burlingame
   California
   94010

   1780 Howard Ave.
   Burlingame, CA 94010

   X Yes

   Burlingame
   California
   94010

   May 2, 1988

   Linda Garrison
   May 2, 1988

C. Addressing an Envelope

Ex. L-3

Student's
Return
Address

Mrs. Karen Bernard
48 Elk St.
Aurora, Illinois 60505

1. In the zip code book in the post office. Sometimes they are in the telephone book.
2. Something fragile, like a photograph, is inside.
   It's a personal letter for an individual usually in an office.

IV. Reading (page 264)

C. Exercises

1.
   a. 3
   b. 5
   c. 2
   d. 6
   e. 7
   f. 4
   g. 1

2.
   a. T
   b. F
   c. F
   d. T
   e. F
   f. T
   g. T

3.
   a. journalist/editorial
   b. dishes
   c. gathered around/applauded
   d. background
   e. dual
   f. propose a toast
   g. cater to
   h. reference
   i. appreciate/entertainment
   j. thesaurus
   k. novel
   l. hard-working/struggled

V. Structure (page 266)

Review

Ex. S-1

1. tries
2. Did criticize
3. will publish
4. aren't/reading
5. was broadcasting
6. will be changing
7. haven't seen
8. have been visiting
9. had subscribed
10. had been writing
11. will have finished

Ex. S-2

1. long
2. hopeful
3. exciting
4. visual
5. commercial
6. suspicious
7. sorrowful
8. critical
9. introductory
10. comical

Ex. S-3

1. editor
2. business
3. advertisement
4. classic
5. mystery
6. technique
7. circulation
8. education
9. romance
10. history

Ex. S-4

1. During (At)/at (through)/for/to
2. up/in/in (at)
3. During (At)/about (over)
4. to/with
5. about/on/near (beside)

Ex. S-5

1. That is the man who knows how to sew.
2. We wanted to go to the concert but it was sold out.
3. I would have gone to the exhibit if I hadn't been so busy.
4. She left early because she didn't feel well.
5. Although Bob was tired, he still helped them.

Ex. S-6

1. James left New York at 7 o'clock.
2. He yelled, "What a surprise!"
3. Where did Mr. and Mrs. Horton go?

VII. Pronunciation

A. Teacher can choose one of the pair of words for students to underline.

B.
1. bought	11. rim	21. bat
2. paint	12. full	22. dead
3. zeal	13. flew	23. close
4. fat	14. cap	24. worse
5. sheet	15. run	25. card
6. dawn	16. doll	26. rope
7. joke	17. row	27. gave
8. sound	18. shot	28. math
9. nail	19. men	29. wing
10. when	20. bell	30. of

B. Teacher can dictate sentences from previous lessons.

VIII. Life Skills (page 271)

A. Newspaper Contents

Ex. L-1

1. 4 (A, B, C & D)
2. a. Weather A2
   b. Religion A12, 13
   c. Sports B1-6
   d. Lively Arts D4
   e. Editorials D2
3. Advice for playing the card game.
4. (Students answer according to the latest news.)
5. Comics B10
6. a. Births C2
   b. Travel D7
   c. Lifestyle A10, 11

B. Entertainment Guide

Ex. L-2

1. January 7th at 8 P.M., "My Fair Lady"
2. Ira Kane
3. Dinosaur Exhibit plus aquarium and planetarium
4. Go to the Flower Show at Lakeside Garden Center
5. The Redhots
6. Lighthouse theater, Friday, Saturday and Sunday at 8, through the end of the month
7. International folk songs
8. Paintings, sculpture and prints

C. Card Catalogue

Ex. L-3

author/title/subject

1. Subject
2. No
3. Walt Whitman
4. Clement Wood
5. Poets of America
6. Carl Sandburg
7. 1921 and 1925
8. Modern Library and E.P. Dutton & Company
9. 1819-1892
10. 311 pages
11. Hollywood, Movies, Los Angeles